PELICA KU-695-362

EDITED BY V. K. KRISHNA MENON

Advisory Editors ; H. L. BEALES, Reader in Economic
History, University of London; W. E. WILLIAMS,
Secretary, the British Institute of Adult Education;
SIR PETER CHALMERS-MITCHELL, C.B.E., F.R.S., F.Z.S.,
DR.SC., LL.D., Secretary of the Zoological Society
1903—1935

AN OUTLINE OF THE UNIVERSE (I)
BY J. G. CROWTHER

PELICAN BOOKS

AN OUTLINE OF THE UNIVERSE

BY

J. G. CROWTHER

IN TWO VOLUMES: VOLUME ONE

PUBLISHED BY
PENGUIN BOOKS LIMITED
HARMONDSWORTH MIDDLESEX ENGLAND

First published 1931
Published in Pelican Books 1938

MADE AND PRINTED IN GREAT BRITAIN FOR PENGUIN BOOKS LIMITED
BY PURNELL AND SONS, LTD., PAULTON (SOMERSET) AND LONDON

I cannot make record of all in full, seeing that my long theme drives me on, so that oftentimes speech comes short of fact.

DANTE: *Divine Comedy*

CONTENTS OF VOLUME ONE

CHAPTER		PAGE
I.	WHAT THE UNIVERSE IS LIKE	19
II.	ISLAND UNIVERSES	32
III.	THE GALAXY	38
IV.	THE STARS	46
V.	TWIN STARS	49
VI.	STARS IN THEMSELVES	53
VII.	VARIABLE STARS	62
VIII.	THE SUN	67
IX.	THE PLANETS	72
X.	THE CONDITION OF THE PLANETS	76
XI.	PLUTO	82
XII.	THE EARTH	85
XIII.	THE ULTIMATE MATERIALS	90
XIV.	THE ELECTRON	98
XV.	THE PROTON	105
XVI.	RADIO-ACTIVITY	110
XVII.	SPEED OF a-PARTICLES	116
XVIII.	DISINTEGRATION OF THE ATOM	125
XIX.	ANALYSIS OF VICTORIAN ATOMS	130
XX.	ATOMIC STRUCTURE	135
XXI.	THE MIND OF CHEMISTRY AND OF PHYSICS	143
XXII.	COMPOUNDS OF ATOMS	144
XXIII.	CHEMISTRY OF CARBON COMPOUNDS	147
XXIV.	WHAT CAN BE DONE WITH SOLID, LIQUID AND GASEOUS COMPOUNDS	153
XXV.	COLLOIDS	156
XXVI.	FILTRABLE VIRUSES	165
XXVII.	BACTERIA	170
	GLOSSARY	181

LIST OF PLATES IN VOLUME ONE
Between pages 64–65

1. PLUTO: THE PLANET WHOSE EXISTENCE WAS PRE-DICTED BY LOWELL IN 1914 AND DISCOVERED BY TOMBAUGH IN 1930
2. THE HORSE'S HEAD NEBULA
3. THE GLOBULAR CLUSTER OF STARS IN HERCULES
4. N.G.C. 3587. THE OWL NEBULA
5. N.G.C. 7217
6. N.G.C. 4594. ISLAND UNIVERSES
7. NEBULOSITY IN THE PLEIADES
8. U CEPHEI VARYING IN BRIGHTNESS
9. NOVA AQUILAE IN JUNE 1918
10. THE CORONA AT SUN-SPOT MINIMUM
11. SPOTS ON THE SUN AT SUN-SPOT MAXIMUM
12. X-RAY PHOTOGRAPH OF NICKEL SULPHATE CRYSTALS
13. X-RAY PHOTOGRAPH OF BERYL CRYSTAL

Between pages 128–129

14. ONE OF C. T. R. WILSON'S 1912 PHOTOGRAPHS
15. A NITROGEN ATOM DISINTEGRATED
16. A CRETIN AFTER TREATMENT WITH THYROID EXTRACT
17. COLLOIDAL PARTICLES TO WHICH RUBBER OWES ITS PROPERTIES
18. PARTICLE IN LATEX OF A BUD-GRAFT FROM THE SAME MOTHER-TREE—AN EXAMPLE OF INHERIT-ANCE OF A COLLOIDAL CHARACTERISTIC OF A LIVING ORGANISM
19. SVEDBERG'S ULTRA-CENTRIFUGE

PREFACE

THE Universe is often mentioned in conversation, though few have a clear notion of what they mean by the word. This book contains an outline of what the word means for me. I hope the reader will find his notion of the Universe clarified through contrast or similarity by reading a sketch of mine. The vagueness of the modern's notion of the Universe is much more than it might and ought to be, and is a consequence of a lack of comprehensive thinking in recent centuries. It is a reflexion of a period of excessive individualism following the decay of the unified mediæval civilization. In A.D. 1300 a man could describe fairly confidently and clearly his notion of the Universe. The changes of the following centuries brought an increase of knowledge which showed that the mediæval notions of the Universe were seriously defective, so defective that all similar comprehensive thinking became discredited. Men turned to study the minute particular; Vesalius, Galileo, Gilbert and the rest making the first characteristic essays in modern scientific method. During the last four hundred years there has been a reaction from the general to the particular. It is related to the rapid evolution of civilization; when the organization of society is changing rapidly comprehensive notions of the Universe are difficult to form. Recent history seems to show the reaction has become excessive. Everywhere there is a concentration on the particular and a neglect of the general, and indeed an exhibition of this attitude is considered a sign of wisdom. A physicist expressing an opinion on biology is in danger of committing a minor crime, the commercial shrewdness of a business man who discusses art intelligently is suspect. England's cricket eleven has a tail because batsmen no longer bowl nor bowlers bat, great wars occur because men specialize on their own and their nation's advantage rather than work for the advantage of humanity. The current of four hundred years' striving has narrowed to a race of specialization in which the typical man works intensely at his job and is ignorant of nearly all other indirectly related things. American industrial magnates whose special genius has been overwhelmingly demonstrated are found to have no conversation and to spend nearly all of their somnambulist out-of-office hours playing bridge and golf, duck-shooting, and indulging in a hundred other activities transformed from recreations into mental opiates. Four hundred years ago the new idea of specialization was divine and threw an illuminating beam which discovered the miraculous movement and design of the succeeding centuries. The old idea of comprehensiveness waned until to-day it is hidden by the inco-ordinated pile of knowledge gained by specialization. Everywhere there is brilliance; in science, in industry, in sport, but the setting for the brilliants is inadequate. People have now to relearn the habit of trying to see the Universe. Their data are incomparably richer than those of the Middle Ages and should inspire a more wonderful vision. Perhaps as the habit returns the modern muddles in industry and politics will seem unbearably fatuous, and men will require elegance in the organization of society as they would in a scientific theory. If the Universe is viewed clearly, society may be viewed clearly and its insanities seen and removed.

NOTE

THIS book is an essay in a craft still sufficiently new to be ill-defined, the craft of scientific journalism. Since this craft is not yet established a note on its nature may be useful. The function of scientific journalism is to convey the atmosphere and facts of recent scientific research to the public, the conveyance of atmosphere being the more important part. Accuracy of fact is desirable but less important than accuracy of atmosphere. At present scientific journalism is practised mainly by scientists wishing to increase their pocket-money or too elderly to have sufficient energy for research. Their work is sporadic and usually suffers in the first instance from defects in style due to the character of their motive and in the second from the mental deconcentration which affects those within sight of the grave. These types of scientific journalist conceive their work respectively in terms of entertainment and religion. As a proper craft scientific journalism is social. It is becoming an essential binder in the structure of a civilization created by the application of science to industry. Modern society may collapse unless the atmosphere of science becomes generally apprehended. The future will probably require and see an impersonal scientific journalism which expresses the atmosphere and the simpler of the more important facts in every branch of science and not so much the opinions of the writer. Anyone in contact with scientists is aware how often general accounts of recent scientific work give the facts but not the mental attitude of the researchers. For instance, the days' two leaders in theoretical physics are men of about thirty years, their ideas have been generally expounded by men of about fifty years or older and one is certain many of these widely read expositions do not reveal the mentalities of the young creative thinkers. The revolutionary, hard and brilliant intellects of Heisenberg and Dirac do not yield mysticism; that is a spurious growth stimulated in uncreative by creative minds. Mysticism is the product of those who fail to understand, the substitute for comprehension and the margarine of philosophy. The scientific journalist's attitude must be adopted from that of creative workers and he must attempt to convey what these workers think and do. He must assume scientific authorities are right about matters in their own branches of research. He must be aware that however vitalist distinguished experimental biologists pretend to be, in the laboratory where their fame was achieved they are observed to be strictly mechanist. Civilization requires, or at least one interested hopes it requires, the establishment of a scientific journalism which demands the entire intellectual attention of those who practise it. The proper scientific journalist should devote the whole of his intellectual energy to the prosecution of his craft. Then society will learn from continuous impersonal accounts that attitude required to solve present social problems, and will scorn sporadic writing intended to titivate its humour or its soul.

ACKNOWLEDGMENTS

I AM much indebted to several scientific friends for reading parts of my manuscript and reducing the number of errors. I owe much to books by A. S. Eddington, J. B. S. Haldane, A. V. Hill, J. S. Huxley, J. H. Jeans, T. H. Morgan, C. K. Ogden, H. N. Russell, G. E. Smith, G. P. Wells, H. G. Wells, and other authorities. The titles are given in a bibliography for further reading.

The following authors, societies, publishers and firms have kindly given me permission to reproduce illustrations: Mr. W. T. Astbury, Dr. P. M. S. Blackett, Dr. G. C. Bourne, Sir William Bragg, Dr. W. Chesterman, Dr. F. Martin Duncan, Dr. H. B. Fell, Professor A. V. Hill, Dr. C. O. Jensen, Mme. Roberts, Professor Elliot Smith, Professor Svedberg, Professor C. T. R. Wilson; the Royal Society, the Royal Astronomical Society, the *Journal of Heredity*, the *Lancet*, the *Quarterly Journal of Microscopy*, Messrs. E. Arnold & Co., Ltd., Messrs. Bell & Co., Ltd., Messrs. Cape & Co., Ltd., Messrs. Chatto & Windus, Ltd., Messrs. Gyldenhal & Co., Ltd., Messrs. Macmillan & Co., Ltd., Messrs. G. Newnes & Co., Ltd., and the Oxford University Press.

BIBLIOGRAPHY

A Manual of Astronomy, by H. N. Russell and Young. (Ginn.)

The Universe Around Us, by Sir J. H. Jeans. (Camb. Univ. Press.)

Stars and Atoms, by Sir A. S. Eddington. (Oxford University Press.)

X-rays and Crystal Structure, by Sir William and W. L. Bragg. (Bell.)

The Atom, by E. N. de C. Andrade. (Bell.)

The Science of Life, by H. G. Wells, J. S. Huxley and G. P. Wells. (Newnes.)

Animal Biology, by J. B. S. Haldane and J. S. Huxley. (Clarendon Press.)

Evolution and Genetics, by T. H. Morgan. (Princeton Univ. Press.)

Living Machinery, by A. V. Hill. (Bell.)

Human History, by G. Elliot Smith. (Cape.)

The A B C of Psychology, by C. K. Ogden. (Kegan Paul.)

AN OUTLINE OF THE UNIVERSE

I

WHAT THE UNIVERSE IS LIKE

SCIENTISTS are not decided on the finiteness or infinite-ness of the Universe. Astronomers are inclined to consider it finite. If it were not, the number of stars might be infinite and the night sky a blaze of light, since there would be no gaps between the stars. If the stars were fairly evenly scattered through an infinite universe, it would be necessary only to travel far enough in any direction to come to one, assuming the sky were perfectly transparent.

If space were occupied at various places by obscuring clouds of matter, a rough-and-ready argument of this kind would be vitiated, and as such clouds are known it cannot be taken very seriously.

Some physicists, impressed more by theoretical than practical contradictions, incline to an infinite universe. If it were, the paradox of the "running-down" universe would not then arise. That hot things tend to cool down and cold things to warm up to a steady average temperature is well known, and we can imagine the destiny of the matter of the Universe is a condition of uniform temperature in which nothing further ever happens. This end would appear to be inevitable in a finite universe. Now if the Universe has a final state, presumably it had an initial state, which implies the necessity of supposing it was miraculously created some-time in the past. In any case, if the Universe has existed from all eternity and is developing into a final state at a known rate, why didn't it reach the final state aeons ago?

If the Universe is infinite, there may well be an infinite supply of hot matter or free energy in it, and some may always be flowing into that part of the Universe with which we are familiar.

According to the theory of relativity, the Universe may be either finite or infinite. As astronomers incline to regard it as finite, and the idea of a finite universe is the more novel and hence the more stimulating to the reader, we will assume provisionally the Universe is finite.

According to Hubble, its volume is of the order 384,000,000,000, billion, billion, billion, billion cubic miles.

This limited thing is seen to contain matter, space and time.

Until recently space and time were believed to exist more or less independently of each other and that entirely empty space could quite possibly exist by itself, or time just go on by itself, and that both could get on perfectly well without matter. Matter, space and time are now believed to be organically inter-related; flesh of one flesh, bone of one bone, as it were. Expressed in scientific terms, this belief is known as the theory of relativity. If in anything matter changes, then space and time change in it, too. We have now to imagine space and time as plastic and not rigid abstractions.

The notion of plasticity appeals particularly to the artistic sense, perhaps that is why the theory of relativity was discovered by a scientist whose mentality is exceptionally artistic.

Einstein is not a mathematician of the highest order, his mathematical methods are often clumsy and the original proofs incomplete. But he has the faculty of divining scientific truths and constructing rough, pioneer, mathematical paths towards them. After he has seen the light and prospected the way the mathematicians swiftly civilize the path, and manufacture a short and elegant promenade, at the end of which the new truth shines obviously.

The Universe is finite, but unbounded. The surface of the earth is also finite and unbounded. You can walk straight on in front of you for ever; there will always be surface in front of you to walk on. The same sort of thing happens in the total orb of space; though its volume is finite, a traveller through it will always find fresh space to traverse opening before him.

It is easy to see that you could make an infinitely long journey by travelling around the Earth's Equator for ever. You would retrace your steps and sails continuously, piling up the endless miles in repeating sections about 25,000 miles long, the length of the Equator. But it is not obvious at once that you could make an infinitely long journey on the finite but unbounded surface of the earth, without retracing or recrossing your path, yet this is quite possible.

Suppose a man starts walking spirally from the North Pole towards the Equator, and that the latitudinal distance between adjacent paths continuously diminishes, and approaches zero but never actually becomes nothing (fig. 1). That there can be an infinite number of journeys round the earth without ever reaching the Equator is clear, and that nearly all of these journeys will approach 25,000 miles in length, hence it is possible to travel an infinite distance on the finite surface of the earth without ever once retracing one's steps or recrossing one's path. A ray of light journeying on through the finite space of the Universe without retracing or recrossing its path may be conceived similarly. The importance of this point will be obvious in relation to the problem of where the light of the stars goes to. If the Universe is finite, how is it that light from a star does not, so far as we know, go right round the Universe and arrive back at the star? Because light tracks in space may perhaps have qualities similar to that infinitely long non-retracing

or recrossing spiral path possible on the Earth's finite
surface.

Matter, space and time are organically inter-related.
If matter changes, space and time change too. Since
matter is always changing, so must space and time.
We have to imagine the Universe as a plastic, palpitating complex of matter, space and time. It is more
like a trembling, expanding soap-bubble than a crystal

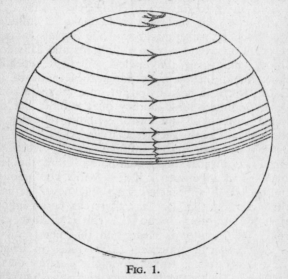

FIG. 1.

sceptre. When a particle of matter moves the strains
and bends of space in its neighbourhood are changed.

If a being could survey the Universe from outside,
that is, from a view-point in the fifth dimension, he
would see a finite palpitating object, corresponding to
something like a trembling and expanding bubble.
He would, perhaps, be more interested in the geometry
and motions of what appeared to him as the confines
of our Universe, and not so much in the shining specks
and other insignificant particles floating inside.

But for beings inside the Universe shining specks and other minute and adjacent trifles would possess fascination. Would they, though? Perhaps those perverse beings might persistently prefer the unseen to the seen, for it is easier to appreciate the mystery in the unseen than in the seen. If the objects of discussion are evident, it is easier to test the truth of assertions about them. If it is asserted that an object is round, and constructed in a certain way, well, it is necessary only to examine the object to discover whether the assertion is true.

Assertions about the seen are more dangerous than those about the unseen, because it is possible to verify the truth of the assertions about the seen, and thus test the intelligence and character of the seer.

Perhaps that is why science is the latest flowering of the cultures.

A cursory examination of the Universe from the inside reveals an immense but finite extent of nearly empty space. About 2,000,000 minor or island universes are seen to be hurtling bodily through the tenuity at speeds of the order of 1,000 miles a second, and probably there are many millions more beyond the range of our telescopes. To observers on the Earth these hurtling minor universes appear as nebulae. They are scattered throughout space fairly evenly. If a telescope is particularly directed to the heavens there is about as much chance of seeing an island-universe nebula in that as in any other direction. Being evenly scattered through space, they appear evenly scattered over the heavens.

The immense speeds at which they recede may be due to the continuous expansion of space itself as if it were being blown up like a balloon, a possibility allowed by the theory of relativity. The effects of this expansion may not be large enough to be evident within our local universe, but at the distance of the extra-local universes the effect might be large. It has

been estimated that space doubles its radius every
1,400,000,000 years. If this is true the island universes
seen as extra-galactic nebulae are ephemeral objects
racing out of our sight. In an astronomically short
interval the nebulae will have disappeared from the
part of space observable by us and beings existing
on the earth at that time would observationally be
ignorant of island universes besides their own. Oddly,
the recession of the spiral nebulae enables the number
of particles in the universe to be estimated; it comes
out at 1.4×10^{79}, i.e. 14 followed by 78 noughts.

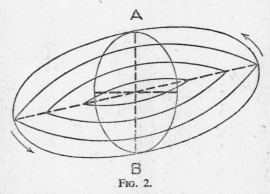

FIG. 2.

An Ellipsoid: the kind of figure into which groups of stars and
nebulae form themselves to constitute an island universe.

What are those island universes like? Do they contain peculiar, unimaginable things? They appear in
many varieties, and of one at least it is possible to
gain some detailed knowledge, for we ourselves career
in a particular island universe. All the stars visible to
the naked eye are members of our local island universe.
Its general shape is at once evident. It is a disc-shaped
Galaxy mainly of stars, for the Milky Way reveals
the section to be seen when a being inside this Galaxy
looks towards the rim.

Study reveals that island universes, including our own, are usually shaped like a squashed Rugby football. They are roughly symmetrical about their axes of length, breadth and thickness, but the lengths of these axes differ.

The island universe usually rotates about one of the short axes, say A B in fig. 2, the arrows showing the direction of rotation. We have, then, to imagine space as speckled with island universes flying and spinning as a starry Rugby football would fly and spin when kicked through the air.

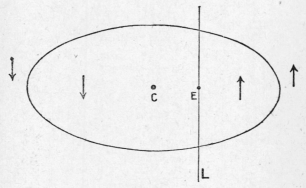

Fig. 3.

Our own local universe behaves like that. It is flying bodily at a great speed relative to the other nebulae in space. It spins about one of its short axes. This is proved by the phenomenon of star-streaming. When the motions of stars are carefully measured, it is found that they can be divided, on the average, into two streams. These are the opposite rims of the disc of the universe.

Suppose an island universe is rotating in the plane of the page about the axis perpendicular to the page through C. Then to an observer within the universe at a point E, the stars to the right of E will, on the average, appear to be streaming in a direction opposite to those on the left of E. Moreover, the stars on the right will appear to be streaming slower than those on the left, because E is, on the average, nearer to them.

Recently the two streams of stars observable in the Galaxy have been shown to be an effect of radial rather than rotatory streaming. Apparently the stars are approaching the centre of the Galaxy more as comets approach the Sun. The streams of stars we observe are those approaching and those receding from the centre. The centre of the Galaxy does not become congested, because the stars approaching it increase their pace due to increased gravitational attraction, and thus are able to hurry quickly out of the region, as comets hurry around the Sun. This conception of the galactic rotation is more complicated than that of a simple biscuit rotating on its shortest axis.

These effects have been detected in our own Galaxy, and are a proof that the solar system is at a great distance from the centre. It is estimated that the Galaxy rotates once in 300,000,000 years.

The island universes are all so immensely distant that it is difficult to learn much directly at present, without more powerful telescopes, of their internal constitution, but it is reasonable to assume that they resemble the Galaxy, either as it was, it is, or it will be.

Examination of our own Galaxy reveals a variety of bodies, but a variety infinitely less extensive than might be expected. Just as it is astonishing to discover that the totality of space is primarily inhabited by a limited number of rather similar island universes, so is it astonishing to learn that island universes and the Galaxy are inhabited by bodies exhibiting unexpected uniformities. The naked-eye examination of the heavens does not mislead in one impression at least. All the stars appear as uniformly colourless shining points (many would have to look twice before perceiving that Betelgeuse is reddish, while Rigel is bluish). In fact, the vault of stars is much less aesthetically fascinating than is commonly admitted. How many persons of sound taste could really spend hours every clear night enjoying such vision of the stars perceptible to the naked eye ? Far fewer than it is conventional to admit.

Why aren't the heavens lighted by all shapes and sizes of coloured stars and shining nebulae ? Is it really true that the stars are more beautiful than the lights of New York ? To my naked eye they are not more beautiful, only scientific research in inventing giant telescopes and delicate instruments reveals their beauty by deeper observation, and the discovery of aesthetically satisfying theories explaining their nature and behaviour.

Instead of the Universe containing chaotic varieties of bodies comprehensive uniformities are found. It appears all visible stars lie within a comparatively small range of mass, the greatest is no more than about 400 times as massive as the least, or more than about one hundred times as massive as the Sun. They vary greatly in candle-power, but are roughly equal in mass. To the naked eye there is variation in candle-power, but uniformity in apparent size.

Within the Galaxy there are numerous nebulae. These are quite different from the nebulae outside the Galaxy. They are in the main gaseous, being shining volumes of exceedingly tenuous gas. They might be regarded as exceedingly diffuse stars or parents of stars.

Then there are dark nebulae. These probably consist of particles of dust whose diameters are about equal to the wave-lengths of visible light. Clouds of such particles, though exceedingly diffuse, can be excessively opaque. For instance, a small quantity of powder is sufficient to create a huge, intensely black smoke-screen, as ships and aeroplanes use during war. It is not generally understood that the mass of the total of smoke particles in such a cloud is quite negligible compared with the mass of air in it (Plate II).

The star-clusters form another pronounced uniformity in the Galaxy. They are ball-shaped conglomerations of stars, and mark out the ellipsoidal shape of the Galaxy, a few marking the rim, and others the layers towards the centre of the Galaxy, increasing in closeness and number towards the centre. There are about seventy of them. After clusters there are apparently individual stars. But examination reveals that many of these are moving in groups or very open clusters. In fact, the Galaxy may not contain clusters and individual stars, but rather be an intermixture of a number of very large open clusters, of which apparently close clusters and stray stars are but parts (Plate III).

Study of apparently single stars proves that many of them are not single, but twin, or triplet or more. It has been estimated that perhaps 50 per cent. of the stars are twins. If that is true, then the chances were even that the celestial penny had decreed the Sun must be a single instead of a twin star.

Apart from mass, there is an extensive variety in brightness, colour, size, temperature, variability and other characteristics.

Planets form the next order of celestial object. Unfortunately, no telescope in existence is sufficiently powerful to detect planets except in the solar system. As we know only of the planets in our own little solar system they have a slightly vulgar familiarity. Some assert we can almost see the grass growing on one of them, the planet Mars.

Since the Sun's planets are the only ones we know, knowledge of planets is both less and more than of other celestial objects. We cannot compare their properties with those of any other star's planets, but we can obtain much exact and detailed knowledge of them because they are so comparatively near to the Earth.

The uniformities in the Sun's family of planets are striking.

Their distances from the Sun are roughly proportional in most cases to the numbers 4, 7, 10, 16, 28, 52, 100, 196, 388. These are derivable from the series

0, 1, 2, 4, 8, 16, 32, 64, 128 by multiplying by three.

0, 3, 6, 12, 24, 48, 96, 192, 384 and adding four to each.

This fact was noted by Bode in 1772. If the planets are represented diagrammatically as in fig. 4, according to their diameters and distances from the Sun, it is noticed that the fattest tend to lie in the middle of the cigar-shaped figure drawn to envelop them, with the smallest at the ends of the figure. Neptune and the new planet Pluto do not fit the series well.

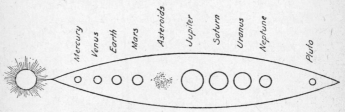

FIG. 4 (after Jeans).

All the planets revolve round the Sun in the same direction.

These uniformities point to some common origin of the planets; they must probably have been created at the same time, or come into existence under the operation of similar systems of forces.

The next series of celestial bodies are the satellites of planets, the most prominent being the Moon. Neptune, Uranus, Saturn and Jupiter all have satellites very much smaller than themselves. Of the inner planets, the Earth is the only one with a satellite, and its satellite the Moon is quite comparable in size with the Earth. Thus the Moon is strikingly different in this particular of the relation of its size to that of its planet from other satellites. We might therefore expect that there is some fundamental difference between the Moon and the satellites of other planets. Research has indeed suggested that this is so, and that the Moon was born by splitting off the rotating Earth, while the satellites of other planets were in general born at the same time as the planets themselves, being concentrations out of the same stuff from which the planets themselves concentrated.

After satellites various small bodies are known, asteroids, shooting stars and comets. The former are a group of small bodies up to 400 miles in diameter revolving round the Sun in the space between Mars and Jupiter. If the whole of them could be impounded into one mass, they might make a planet to occupy exactly the orbit indicated by Bode's law between Mars and Jupiter.

The comets are small groups of stones or chunks of rock up to a few miles in diameter performing orbits round the Sun. Shooting stars are single stones flying into our atmosphere and being burnt up by friction as they rush through the air at a speed of many miles per second. The stone making a bright shooting star may weigh no more than a small fraction of an ounce.

Thus the Universe is made up of entities of the following range of size (one billion = one million million):

	Diameter.	Mass.
(1) The Universe .	1,400,000,000 light-years	Ten billion billion suns.
(2) Island Universes	30,000–300,000 light-years	2,000–200,000 million suns.
(3) Star-Clusters .	2–100 light-years	100,000 suns.
Gas Nebulae .	One billion miles	10,000 suns.
(4) Stars . .	4,000–400,000,000 miles	¼–100 suns.
(5) Planets . .	4,000–80,000 miles	Earth = 6,000 million billion tons.

	Diameter.	Mass.
(6) Satellites . .	20–4,000 miles	Moon = 75 million billion tons.
(7) Asteroids, Comets, etc.	480 miles, downwards	One million billion tons downwards.
(8) Loose terrestrial objects, such as stones, plants, mammals	Big trees: 300 feet high	1,000 tons downwards.
(9) Shooting stars, insects, men, etc., simple plants, etc.	Fractions of an inch to a few feet	200 lb. down to fractions of an ounce.
(10) Particles of dust, microbes, viruses, etc.	$\frac{1}{1,000}-\frac{1}{100,000}$ of an inch	One ten-thousandth of an ounce.
(11) Colloids, filtrable viruses	$\frac{5}{1,000,000}-\frac{1}{10,000}$ of an inch	One thousand million millionths of an ounce.
(12) Stray atoms .	$\frac{1}{100,000,000}$ of an inch	About 50 million billionths of an ounce
(13) Stray electrons and protons	1.5×10^{-13} inches	2.5 thousand million billionths of an ounce.
(hydrogen atom's nucleus)	10^{-16} inches	5 million billionths of an ounce.

Having roughly enumerated the types of objects in the Universe, each type will now be considered in greater detail, though not necessarily in the order of size.

II

ISLAND UNIVERSES

THE island universes appear as nebulae lying vast distances away from our own local universe of stars, how distant may be estimated from their brightness. The brightest is the Great Nebula in Andromeda and is equal in brightness to that of a fourth-magnitude or rather insignificant naked-eye star. A whole universe of thousands of millions of stars, and yet it shines with no more apparent brightness than one of the minor local stars. If the lights of a city appear in the distance as no brighter than a spot of light, the city must be exceedingly distant.

By methods presently to be explained, this nebula is known to be nearly 1,000,000 light-years away. That is, about six million, million, million miles away. The light by which the Andromeda nebula is seen started coming here a million years ago, before man himself had appeared on the Earth. Hundreds of thousands of island universes are seen as extra-galactic nebulae, and all are fainter than the Andromeda. Assuming they are roughly the same in size, and hence shine with about equal candle-power or sun-power, simple proportion shows the faintest of the observed island nebulae must be at least 140 times farther away than the Andromeda nebula, i.e. 140 million light-years away. The light which faintly penetrates to the Earth and slowly blackens the silver salts in the photographic plate at the eye-piece of the giant telescope must have started from the nebula at 186,000 miles a second and reached us after travelling at that speed for 140 million years. When the light started life had not been born upon Earth comparatively long. In fact, 140 million years is not a negligible fraction of the life of the Earth, say one-fortieth of its age.

Hubble estimates space does not extend ten times beyond the distance of the faintest observable island universe, so it might be said we can see into one-thousandth of the whole volume of space.

About 97 per cent. of the observed island-universe nebulae have distinctly regular shapes. They are often disc-like, having a dominating centre of shining material surrounded by rings of stars. The typical edge-on view and flat view are evident from Plates V and VI.

Between all the shapes there is seen to be definite relation. There are globular island-universe nebulae which seem to consist mainly of a uniformly shining core. Then there are slightly ellipsoidal ones, which look as if they were flattened specimens of the globular type. Still more flattened nebulae appear as lenticular sharpish-edged objects, and other nebulae as thin discs.

A large proportion of these nebulae have spiral marks in them. In some the shining core is large, with the spirals closely coiled to it. Then there are others, so that the nebulae could be arranged in a sequence according to the closeness and openness of the spirals. In many of the nebulae the spirals contain knots, undoubtedly of stars. The knots are always most notable in the outer parts of the spiral, as if the material there had condensed into stars before the more uniform core had begun to differentiate itself.

The fact that the island universes can be arranged in a regular sequence of shapes from the uniform sphere to the disc-like spotty aggregation conveys tounding knowledge to the human mind. It suggests that all island universes pass through a certain mode of existence, starting as spherical uniformities and ending as disc-like aggregations of celestial particles, or stars. The island universes resemble each other as men do, or at least as mammals resemble each other. Those observable are at various stages of their existence, some at the beginning, others nearing their final state. The mere sequence of shapes suggests as much, but mathematical investigation almost proves it. The researches of Jeans and others have shown that great masses of rotating and cooling matter would pass through such a sequence of shapes as is observed to exist in the heavens.

The apparent brightness and superficial shape of island-universe nebulae are sufficient to show their immense remoteness and their subjection to an evolutionary existence. A careful study of the light arriving from them reveals much more confirming evidence. It was learnt that all island-universe nebulae send very similar collections of rays. When their light is resolved into its various components it is seen to resemble the light from stars like the sun. This resolution is very difficult to achieve, because the nebula rays are so faint. To photograph the rays takes many hours, and the plate has to be exposed. The astronomer must uncover his plate each night only when the nebula has been focussed on to it exactly. It would not do to have half a dozen exposures, each with the image of the nebula slightly displaced, so that, in the end, only a blurred photograph resulted. Between each exposure, the Earth must have turned round through most of one revolution and the telescope have journeyed a mighty distance through space before being again directed exactly at that nebula.

From exposures up to eighty hours, remarkable details of the rays have been learned.

The photographs of the resolved light, or spectra, of the island-universe nebulae show that the light from all of the nebulae has substantially the same constitution. Whatever the shape, globular, spiral or irregular, the nebulae emit a mixture of rays made up according to a fairly uniform recipe. The light from the core of the nebulae closely resembles that from stars like the Sun, while the light from the outer parts and edges is usually bluer.

This information indicates that these nebulae are galaxies of stars or matter in the stage of being differentiated into stars. The similarity of light from nebulae of such a variety of shapes suggests that the quality of the light depends on a statistical phenomenon, that there is a very large number of different sorts of stars in each of the nebulae. Suppose there were 10,000 million stars in one nebula and 100 million in another nebula of entirely different superficial aspect, then there would still be enough room for variety in 100 million stars for the collective quality of light to be much the same as for 10,000 million. If there were only a handful of stars in the nebula, the light might be entirely different from the normal because these few stars happened to be of a particular type. The fact that the island-universe nebulae emit light of a complicated but fairly definite mixture is a strong indication that these nebulae really are island universes, enormous aggregates of stars or material in process of condensation into stars.

Observation is directly proving these indications to be correct. The outer parts of various island-universe nebulae have definitely been resolved into stars by the great telescopes. The completion in America of the new giant telescope with a reflector 200 inches in diameter should greatly increase the number of nebular resolutions already achieved.

Besides revealing that the quality of island-universe nebulae light is such as would be expected from vast aggregates of stars, these studies of nebular light reveal much of the movements of these nebulae. Those who sail on the sea have often noticed that the rhythm of waves seems to vary according to whether the boat is sailing across, with or against the waves. If the boat is sailing with the waves, trough succeeds trough slower than if sailing across the waves, and quicker

if against the waves. Similar phenomena occur with
all wave motions, as Doppler pointed out. Since light
has wave-motion characteristics, the same effects are
detected with it. If you are in a celestial boat, say
the earth, and are sailing into or away from the light-
waves radiated from a nebula, the normally red light
from the nebula would look either a little more orange
than usual or a little darker red. Thus by examining
the nebula's rays of light it is possible to discover
whether it is receding or approaching us, and whether
different parts of the nebula are in relative movement.

Once more, the uniformity of the results is astonishing. It is revealed that seven-eighths of the island
universes are receding from us at enormous speeds,
from 300 to 1,800 kilometres per second. Whole island
universes hurtling through space at speeds of one or
two million miles per hour !

A study of these motions indicates that our own local
island universe is moving bodily in a certain direction
through space at a speed of 200 miles per second.
When allowance is made for our own Galaxy's motion,
it is found that every other island universe is receding
from our region in space at average speeds of 1,500,000
miles per hour ! It is difficult to believe that we are
really worthy of such unanimous celestial distaste,
and it is thought that the universal flight from us must
be apparent and not real. There are theoretical grounds
for such a possibility. According to certain forms of
the theory of relativity very distant bodies should show
the effects of the curvature of space. These would be
manifested by the apparent lengthening of the light-
waves from the nebulae. In that case, the observed
lengthening would be due not to the effect of Doppler
but to the bend in space becoming noticeable at exceedingly great distances.

Whether or not the curvature or expansion-of-space
effect accounts for the uniformity of recession of the

nebulae from us, there is no doubt that many of them must have enormous real bodily speeds. Yet in spite of these speeds they are not sensibly observed to move in the heavens year by year. If an object moving at a million miles an hour does not seem to get anywhere even after centuries, it must be colossally far away.

The same spectroscopic methods show that these nebulae are rotating round their centres. In the Andromeda nebula material about one-thirtieth of the radius from the centre is rotating round the centre at 47 miles per second. In the nebula N.G.C. 4594 the rotational speed of the matter about half-way from the centre is about 200 miles per second.

The most accurate methods of measuring the distance of island universes employ Miss Henrietta Leavitt's remarkable discovery concerning a certain kind of variable star, of which the Polestar is an example. These stars are known as Cepheids, after δ Cephei, the characteristic example. It is known that the period of their variation from maximum brightness to maximum brightness, say fifteen hours or five and one-third days, or whatever it is, is exactly related to their absolute candle-power. Hence the absolute candle-power of any Cepheid star can be written down as soon as its period is known.

Telescopic research reveals that there are Cepheids in most of those nebulae which have been at all resolved into stars. After measuring their apparent brightness and their period, it is easy to calculate their absolute brightness and their distance. In this way, the Andromeda nebula is shown to be 1,000,000 light-years away.

It might be objected that these Cepheids are not in the nebula but happen only to be in the line of sight. Observation shows that all of the more completely observed Cepheids are in or near nebulae. Cepheids do not appear isolated in space.

Since the distance of the Andromeda nebula is known, it is easy to calculate its absolute from its apparent candle- or sun-power. It appears to the naked eye as a star of the fourth magnitude. Such a star at the nebula's distance would have to be one and a half million million times as bright as the Sun. Evidently the nebula is an aggregation of millions of stars.

By assuming that in the inner portion of this nebula the centrifugal force due to rotation equals the gravitational attraction of the central mass, calculation shows the whole nebula must be of the order 1,000,000,000 times that of the Sun. Here again is evidence that the nebula is a Galaxy of stars, born or unborn.

III

THE LOCAL ISLAND UNIVERSE: THE GALAXY

HAVING visualised the entire Universe as a region of space-time populated by island universes usually about 1,000,000 light-years apart and with almost pure emptiness between them, it is easier to understand the perspective of our own Galaxy. We should expect to learn that the Galaxy contains thousands of millions of stars, and that comparatively simple isolated objects appearing in it belong to it. If such simple objects did not belong to it, their distance would have to be comparable with that of the island universes. Consequently their components would have to be incomparably huge for the objects to be noticeably visible. Suppose, for instance, that a group of a few hundred stars were upwards of a million light-years away. Each star would have to be incomparably large for the group to appear to us as bright as the Andromeda nebula.

Thus systems of that size must belong to the Galaxy if they are at all noticeable.

We can confidently assume and classify all the simpler noticeable celestial objects as members of the Galaxy.

The stars, star-clusters, the groups of stars such as the constellations, local nebulae too small and simple and of the wrong constitution to be island universes, are among the constituents of the local universe.

Star-clusters can be divided into two classes, globular clusters and open clusters. The first class are very remarkable objects.

They are extraordinarily uniform in shape, and the decrease in star-density from the centre outwards follows a definite mathematical law. Such uniformity indicates the simple operation of physical forces. The mode of operation has not yet been discovered, but probably will be fairly soon. The brightest of the globular clusters appears to the naked eye as a hazy fourth magnitude star, ω Centauri. It is estimated that the brightest of them contain at least 50,000 stars, and probably several times as many more. All of the stars in them are very faint, which suggests that the clusters are very distant.

Owing to the failure to observe Cepheid and other variable stars in most of these clusters their distance is rather difficult to determine. Shapley has solved the problem by discovering that the brightest stars in all clusters are all of the same magnitude. Thus the distance of a cluster can be calculated directly from the apparent magnitude of the brightest stars in it. If this cannot be done, then the distance can be estimated roughly from the apparent diameter of the cluster. On the average, the smaller the apparent diameter, the more distant the cluster.

These methods show that ω Centauri is about 21,000 light-years distant, while the Hercules cluster is 230,000 light-years away.

The total light from a globular cluster is about 300,000 times that of the Sun, and the total mass probably several hundred thousand times that of the Sun.

The distribution of the globular clusters in the heavens is the most extraordinary of all the facts about them. There are seventy of these clusters, and nearly all of them are in one-half of the sky. Not only that, measurement of their distances shows they are distributed regularly about a region 60,000 odd light-years from the Sun. This place coincides with the centre of the Milky Way, and the outer globular clusters

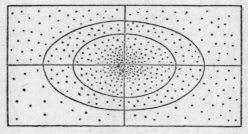

Fig. 5.

mark the confines of the local universe. Thus the local universe is deduced to be ellipsoidal in shape, about 300,000 light-years or more in diameter and 60,000 light-years thick (fig. 5).

The Sun is in a local cluster of stars a long way from the centre of the Galaxy. This follows from the fact that nearly all the globular clusters appear to be on one side of it.

Many years ago Gould noticed that bright stars visible to the naked eye tend to lie roughly in a plane inclined slightly to the plane of the Milky Way. This local plane of concentration marks the relation of our local star-cluster to the local universe.

This fact has had an interesting influence on the
history of the other method of determining the shape
of the local universe, which instead of locating the
outer bounds by measuring the distances of the globular
clusters and working inwards, works outwards from a
study of the distribution of the stars near the Sun.
This method was patiently and profoundly applied by
the distinguished Dutch astronomer Kapteyn. He
showed that as the distance from the region of the
Sun increased, the number of stars per unit volume
decreased. This star distribution showed that stars
even up to great distances from the Sun are arranged
in a group of ellipsoidal form concentrated in the

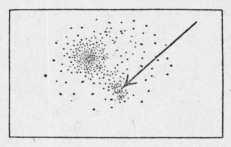

FIG. 6.

centre. When stars were classified according to their
speed, the high-speed stars appeared probably to form
a large loose system beyond the local ellipsoidal concentration demonstrated by Kapteyn. The shape of
the local universe determined from the distribution
of globular clusters was similar to that determined by
the statistical distribution of individual stars, but
enormously larger. The method developed by Shapley
seemed to give a result incompatible with that developed
by Kapteyn. The contradiction has been reconciled,
for Kapteyn's local universe is now agreed to be really
only a part; it is a large local cluster of stars within

the whole, resembling perhaps the local cluster indicated by the arrows on the diagram of Nebula M 33
(fig. 6).

Kapteyn's researches into the average speeds of stars
also first revealed the phenomenon of star-streaming.
He showed that the stars had motions in two preferential
directions which implied that the local universe of
stars was probably rotating about some centre. The
fact that the more distant stars tended to have the
highest speeds fitted this suggestion, since the points
on the hub of a wheel obviously move more quickly
than those on the spokes.

Kapteyn's studies of the number of stars per unit
volume enable estimates to be made of the total number
of stars in the local universe. Workers of his school
place the number at 47,000 million. Since the stars he
most particularly studied are those near the Sun, this
figure applies rather to the local cluster. For the whole
Galaxy Shapley considers 100,000 million nearer the
total. The local universe is very much bigger than
the Andromeda nebula, being about one thousand times
more voluminous. Because of this fact, Shapley
has remarked that if the very distant nebulae are
"islands", then the local universe must be called a
"continent".

Within the local universe there are many nebulae
of types quite different from the island-universe nebulae.
Obviously they must be very much smaller than island
universes, or they could not be contained within the
local universe. That they are smaller is evidenced also
by their frequently greater simplicity.

Galactic nebulae appear green when sufficiently
visible to the observer, whereas the light from the
island-universe nebulae appears white. When their light
is analysed, it is usually found to consist of a comparatively small bundle of rays characteristic of shining
gas, whereas island-universe nebulae emit a jumble of
rays such as a variety of incandescent bodies would

emit. Many galactic nebulae are dark, and some are dark in some parts and light in others, an important fact.

The shapes of the galactic nebulae are of two types, round and diffuse. There are about 150 of the round type, and there is always a faint star in the centre. They are of the order of 700,000,000,000 miles in diameter, and hence the minor details in them must be larger than the solar system. Nevertheless, the planetary nebulae are much smaller than the globular clusters we have been considering. Their masses are about the same as that of the largest stars. Evidently their average density must be exceeding low, if they are not much heavier than the Sun, but enormously more voluminous than the solar system. The density would be about equal to that of a cubic inch of air if it were expanded to a volume of a cubic mile (Plate IV).

They usually complete a rotation around their central star in a period of about 5,000 years. These round planetary nebulae are fairly obviously spheres of rarefied gas illuminated by reflection or by excitation of the light from the central star.

The diffuse type may be bright, dark, or partially bright and partially dark. The latter case shows there is a close connection between the constitution of bright and dark nebulae, and that they are not entirely different sorts of bodies. The simple collections of sharply defined rays into which the light from bright diffuse nebulae can be resolved show that these nebulae consist of rarefied gas. They could not very well be of anything else, because they are so large. For instance, the whole constellation of the Pleiades is enveloped in a diffuse nebula. If it were not very rarefied, its mass would be so enormous that all the local universe of stars would swiftly fall into it under its gravitational attraction (Plate VII).

The diffuse nebulae are exceedingly rarefied gas, and

therefore are probably very cold. How can they shine if they are cold ?

This was explained by Hubble in 1922. He showed that the rays of light from these nebulae are closely related to those from neighbouring hot stars. If the stars were very hot, their energetic rays of light and also of electrons stimulated the atoms of the nebulae gas to emit rays of their own; if the stars were cooler, the nebulae shone more by reflected light.

The illumination of galactic nebulae appears to be indirect, and there is good reason to suppose that only a small portion of the gas in them is in a suitable state to respond to stimulation by rays from the adjacent stars. When there is a large amount of matter in an unsuitable state, the nebula remains dark.

The local universe contains huge dark nebulae. The great split in the Milky Way is probably due to one of colossal extent, estimated to be thousands of light-years in length. Dark nebulae probably obscure much of the brilliantest portions of the centre of the Galaxy, and so have prevented our observing the brilliant central concentration directly, and have caused us to depend more on indirect determinations of its position from the distribution of the globular clusters, star-streaming, etc. They are probably made of particles larger than atoms.

That particles of matter of the same order of size as wave-lengths of light can make clouds of astonishing opacity has been mentioned.

An inch-cube of stone divided into little cubes of side one-tenth of an inch, will provide one thousand of them. These thousand cubes can be fitted together to make an area of ten square inches. Thus the stopping power of the little cubes is ten times that of the parent cube.

If the inch-cube were cut up into cubes of the same

order of wave-lengths of light, the little cubes would have a side of one one-hundred-thousandth of an inch, and there would be one billion of them. These could be arranged in 100,000 slices of one square inch, and consequently would have 100,000 times the stopping power of one inch-cube.

The dark cloud in Ophiuchus, which is 10 light-years long by 5 thick, is estimated to contain no more than a dozen disintegrated suns to lend it its opacity.

Since many of the dark nebulae have definite shapes, their material is probably moving under the influence of its own inter-gravitational attraction. The dust

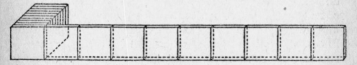

FIG. 7 (10-inch-square slices, each made up of one hundred little cubes.)

particles may continually be bumped together during its gravitational circulations, and large particles will tend to smash each other into dust. Thus there may be a tendency for dark nebulae to become more susceptible to stimulation into shining as their constituent particles become sufficiently reduced in size.

Having reviewed the major objects in the local universe, we step nearer to the mundane, the individual stars, of which our nearest cosmical relation, the Sun, is one.

IV

THE STARS

THE stars and the planets appear to the naked eye about equally bright. We are told planets can be identified because they shine steadily and do not twinkle. Sirius twinkles furiously, and Jupiter does not, but they are roughly equal in apparent brightness. Sirius and the other stars are called fixed. As they do not palpably move across the heavens, they are not planets of the Sun. Newton showed by the principle of gravitation that the stars must be very distant from the Sun, for they would either fall into it or revolve round it if they were reasonably near. If they were very distant, they could not be similar to the planets, because they must be very much more luminous than the planets which shine by reflected light. In order to be visible at those distances, they must be self-luminous bodies similar to the Sun. Newton calculated the Sun would have to be 100,000 times farther away from us than it is if it had appeared to us with Sirius' brightness. If the candle-power of Sirius and the Sun were equal, Newton's result would be correct. This simple and profound argument is characteristic of Newton and reveals the quality of an intellect whose operations are usually obscured from the general view by the dress of mathematics.

Newton's genius resided in a lucid common sense combined with mathematical facility, both gifts being in extraordinary degree.

Analysis of the light from the stars shows they are intrinsically similar to the Sun. When star-light is resolved into component rays the bundle's composition is seen to roughly resemble that of sunlight, though often with wide variation.

The little points of twinkling light called stars are really distant suns. Thus the apparent fixity of the stars is due to their extreme distance. If we could go nearer them we might perceive their places in the sky palpably changing. Suppose the Sun were in the midst of a dense star-cluster. Then the bright stars might appear as bright as the Moon, and in various colours. As we cannot yet travel more than a few thousand feet from the Earth, the nature of the stars must be learned from meticulous observation.

The first valuable tables of careful observation were made by the Greeks, but were lost. Ptolemy gave a table of the positions of 1,025 stars in the year A.D. 137. Claims have been made for the antiquity of various Hindu tables, but the dates of many of these are uncertain. As De Morgan remarked about one of the tables, if the figures given in it referred to the position of stars in the year of compilation, then it must have been compiled in about A.D. 4000 ! The next valuable table was made for Ulugh Beg at Samarkand about A.D. 1450. After that, Tycho Brahe's table of 1,005 stars came in 1580, and was the foundation from which Kepler speculated and discovered his laws.

It is interesting to note that Ptolemy in A.D. 137 and Tycho Brahe 1,443 years later gave particulars of substantially the same number of stars, about one thousand. Why was that ? Because the optical powers of the instruments they used were about the same. They used their own naked eyes. During all those centuries, nothing powerfuller than the naked eye had been used in celestial observations.

The very best naked eye cannot distinctly see more than 3,000 stars on the clearest night. Only about 1,000 of these are susceptible of careful naked-eye observation. That is why Tycho measured no more than Ptolemy.

The stars were early classified into constellations on the basis of apparent proximity. The Pleiades, Orion, the Plough, etc. It is now known that in many cases the proximity is real; many of the stars in the constellations mentioned definitely belong to groups voyaging through space. The very names of the constellations are a source of knowledge, for they show in which countries the names were first applied. The constellations near the North Pole must have been named in Mesopotamia, for the animals are Biblical.

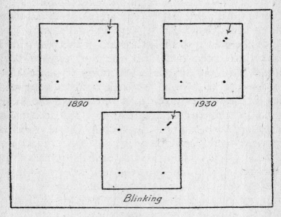

1890   *1930*

Blinking

Fɪɢ. 8.

As there is no tiger or elephant, they could not have been invented in India, nor in Egypt, for there is no crocodile or hippopotamus.

A mere field-glass increases the number of observable stars to 50,000. Argelander observed about 300,000 stars in half the celestial sphere with a 2½-inch telescope. The 100-inch telescope at Mount Wilson reveals one million million photographable stars, 1,500,000,000 in the galactic system. The new 200-inch telescope will probably reveal a large number of billions of stars photographically.

Do the stars move? The most striking proof is given by the "blink" microscope. If two photographs of a group of stars are taken at an interval of years, the plates will look very similar. Careful scrutiny and measurement may reveal that some of the dots representing stars have moved relatively. This laborious process is sound enough, but not a picturesque proof of stellar movement. In the "blink" instrument, the plates are presented to the eye in rapid alternation. Those spots in the same relative positions on both plates appear to remain still, while the spots which have shifted vibrate (Fig. 8).

The "blink" instrument causes a difference in position to be manifested as a motion, and motions are much more noticeable than differences in position.

When the plates for 1891 and 1931 are arranged in the "blink" microscope, the star whose position has changed appreciably appears to vibrate or blink, owing to the plates being alternately exposed to the eye for a fraction of a second.

v

TWIN STARS

It is estimated that half of the stars are twins. More than 20,000 are known to be twin. A considerable number are triplets and some are quadruplets. Their simplicity makes the existence of these stellar systems evident.

The more complicated relations obtaining in groups of stars are much harder to define, but certainly there, since gravitation causes all bodies to attract each other, and stars in compact or globular clusters must move according to definite laws, though these are difficult

to discover because of the complication of having many
bodies affecting each other all at once. The problem
becomes simpler when the number of bodies is very
large, since the laws of statistics then begin to apply.
In large aggregates any peculiar motion can be paired
off with another equal one in the opposite direction,
so that only normal motions need be considered. Hence
the astronomer can discover the laws governing the
motions of simple systems of stars and also of very
complicated ones before he can unravel the laws of
moderately complicated systems. He can deal with
groups of several stars so long as there are pronounced
inequalities in size and distance between them, but he
has not yet solved the behaviour of three bodies of
equal size moving at approximately equal distances
from each other.

When the number of stars in a group is very large
indeed, the group begins to exhibit some of the properties of a gas, which is merely a group of small bodies
called molecules.

A casual inspection of the sky does not suggest that
many stars are twin. A closer inspection shows that
far more stars appear in pairs than chance would war-
rant. Sir William Herschel assumed that twin stars
were chance arrangements due to the stars being in
the same line of sight. He began to observe them
carefully, hoping to discover the rate at which they
separated, but found instead that they tended to revolve
round each other. Many of the stars he observed
were resolved into pairs of points by his telescope. A
century later, when the spectroscope could be used for
measuring the rate at which stars approached or receded
from the Earth, it was discovered that very many stars
behaved as if they were in two parts, which alternately
approached and receded. In fact, the spectrum of the
star appeared to be really two spectra very closely
superimposed, each spectrum pertaining only to one of
the two parts and betraying its behaviour. Evidently

these stars with double spectra were twin stars, but so close together that the powerfullest telescope could not resolve them into twin points of light.

How would two stars similar to the Sun and only a few million miles apart appear to a distant observer as they rotated round each other? If the observer happened to be in or near the plane of the twin stars' mutual revolution, the stars would occasionally get in front of each other. Then only one of them would be visible, and the luminosity of the twin star would be reduced by one-half. If the stars were unequal in candle-power or area, and their plane of revolution oblique to the observer, the changes in apparent candle-power would be more complicated. These various kinds of changes in the apparent candle-power of stars have been observed.

Algol was noticed by Montanari in 1670 to vary in brightness. The star's Arabic name, which means "demon", may indicate that the Arabs knew there was something peculiar about it, possibly the variation in brightness. In 1782 Goodricke showed that these variations were periodic, and occurred every 2 days 20 hours 49 minutes. Yet another hundred years had to pass before Algol was proved to vary because it was continually being eclipsed by a close companion star. About 200 pairs of stars of this eclipsing type are known (Plate VIII).

Three lines of evidence for types of twin stars have been mentioned: (1) direct observation of two stars revolving round each, as made by Herschel; (2) spectroscopic evidence that two very close stars are alternately approaching and receding from us, and hence revolving round each other; (3) certain types of variation in the brightness of stars.

There is a fourth type of twin star, the discovery of which has led to extraordinary consequences. It is the faint or dark companion star. As Sirius is the brightest of stars, careful records of its position in the heavens have been kept for a long time. Like other stars it is drifting through space, and year by year it drifts forward, presumably in a straight line, since apparently there is no proximate star to perturb it. About 80 years ago Bessel showed that the presumption is incorrect. Sirius apparently moves forward, not along a straight but a flat wavy line (fig. 9).

This is just how Sirius would appear to move if a dark companion star were revolving round it. In that case, the centre of gravity of the pair would trace the straight line, while each of the twins would appear to us to trace a wavy path. This is all very well, but though Sirius himself was observed to wave, there was no evident companion. Nevertheless Bessel said that the period of revolution of the dark companion would be

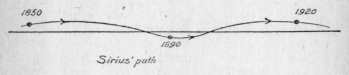

Sirius' path

FIG. 9.

fifty years. In 1862 a maker of telescopes, Mr. Clarke, having finished a new one, happened to direct it to Sirius to see how the new instrument acquitted itself. He was surprised to see a tiny spot of light near the major star. "Dear me" (we may venture in the style of modern biography), "my new telescope lenses must have a flaw in them to show a spot of light where there isn't one. What a nuisance."

Further examination showed the spot was not due to a flaw but to a newly-discovered star. The cause of the wobbling of Sirius had been discovered. When the positions of the faint companion were tabulated, they showed Bessel's prediction, that the time of revolution was fifty years, was correct.

In 1924 the dark companion of Sirius provided still another sensation, but the story of this must wait until a later chapter.

If the time of revolution of twin stars about each other is known, and the size of the ellipses in which they move can be inferred from the waviness in their celestial tracks, their weights can be calculated.

Sirius proves to be about four times the weight of its dark companion, whose own weight is about equal to the Sun's.

Plaskett's remarkable twin star has components respectively 75 and 63 times the weight of the Sun. Each of the components is of about 20,000 times the Sun's candle-power, so the twin star is as luminous as 40,000 suns. Its surface temperature is estimated to be about 28,000° C., nearly five times as hot as the Sun's.

VI

STARS IN THEMSELVES

ALL the stars appear to us as points of light, yet if they are suns their diameters must be at least half a million miles. "The stars are so far away that even with diameters of that size they dwindle to point-apparitions," we say. "I'm getting tired of that sort of excuse," you reply, "whenever I raise any evident difficulty in your story you always say the stars are too far, or too something or other for the character I reasonably expect should be evident, to wit, their diameter. How do I know that all your indirect calculations are correct, and that the stars are not the mere twinkling points they appear to be ? Show me their diameter."

We cannot quite do that because no telescope is powerful enough for the purpose. The biggest telescope is only 100 inches in diameter. However, we can make an instrument which will do as well as a super telescope for this particular purpose.

Suppose you look at a star, using only two bits of the reflecting mirror of your telescope, at A and at B, A and B being at opposite ends of a diameter of the mirror. The central portion of the mirror between A and B is blocked out. When this is done, the image of the star at F is observed to be crossed with dark and bright lines running perpendicular to the direction

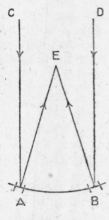

Fig. 10.

A B. These lines are due to the interference of the light-waves following the two different routes D B F, C A F, when they intermix at F. If A and B were closer together, a different series of black and white bands would appear in the image, some of the blacks appearing where there were whites under the first circumstances. When the mirror is entirely uncovered all the blacks and whites are jumbled up, and cancel out. That's why it is necessary to use only bits of the mirror as at A and B.

Suppose now there is another star near to the first. That also will make an image at F banded with dark and bright lines. What should happen if its black lines coincided with the bright lines in the image of the first star? The two images would cancel each other's lines and form one diffuse image. Under what circumstances may this happen? Calculation shows that the nearer the stars are together, the greater the distance A B must be, if the blacks and whites of the

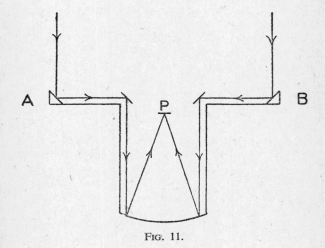

Fig. 11.

two images are to cancel. If the stars are very near, A B proves to be greater than the diameter of the greatest telescope.

As A and B are only parts of the mirror, they can be simulated by mirrors at the ends of a beam. The beam may be any length. At Mount Wilson a beam 20 feet long was used, which enabled the 100-inch mirror to act as if it were a 240-inch mirror for the present purpose, so that A and B were effectively 240 inches apart.

With this arrangement it was possible to measure the distance between very close stars.

"But how does that help you to measure the diameter of one star?" you inquire. Well, one star can be conceived as two.

The centres of brightness of the halves of the star are at X and Y. They can be conceived as two bright discs partly intersecting, i.e., as two exceptionally close stars. So you ought to get the disappearing black and white lines effect even with one star if the distance A B is large enough. It will have to be larger than for any ordinary pair of separate stars.

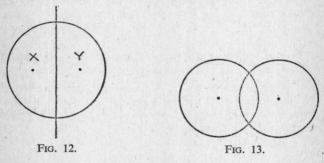

FIG. 12.   FIG. 13.

On December 13th, 1920, the lines were seen to disappear when the contrivance was directed to the star Betelgeuse and adjusted.

The diameter of Betelgeuse proved to be 290,000,000 miles. If the Sun were at the centre of Betelgeuse, the Earth would perform the whole of its orbit inside the star.

Antares is even larger, the diameter being about 400,000,000 miles.

There is the result of a direct measurement of the diameters of stars, a method based on an optical effect due to the spread of the star's shining disc.

A study of the light from the stars reveals more unexpected uniformities. When the various bundles of rays are analysed into their components, their compositions are found to be classified into definite types. The tens of thousands of stars carefully examined can be classified into four main types, which blend into each other in orderly sequence. There is evidently a close relationship between all stars, and the fact that they can be arranged in a continuous sequence of types suggests that the only essential difference between them is stage of evolution; possibly all stars recapitulate the same celestial story, with slight particular variations only.

After evidence of such a profound uniformity, it is not surprising to hear that the light from the stars shows they are made of the same substances as the earth. Iron, oxygen, hydrogen, helium, nitrogen, carbon, titanium, etc., all emit their characteristic light from the stars.

The stellar light not only reveals some of the kinds of matter on the stellar surface, it announces the condition of that matter, its temperature, and density. The temperature of the stellar surface can be inferred from the colour, like that of a hot poker. If the colour is red, the temperature will be about 2,000–3,000° C. If orange, about 4,000° C.; yellow, 5,000–6,000° C.; white, 8,000–11,000° C.; bluish-white, 15,000° C. upwards. The giant star Betelgeuse is red, Arcturus is orange, the Sun is yellow, Sirius is white, Rigel bluish-white. The relation between colour and temperature implies that when a body is at certain temperature it makes more use of some sizes of wave-radiations than of others, for getting rid of its energy. At the temperature of red-heat it makes most use of red-coloured wave-radiations, at blue-heat, of blue radiations. On the Earth substances at blue-heat are not obtainable because blue-heat temperatures of 15,000° C. are not producible in the laboratory. Blue-heat is easily observable in the stars; for instance, in most of the Orion stars. So it is possible to be blue with heat as well as with cold !

The particular relations observed to exist between colour and temperatures can be explained only on the basis of the quantum theory, which states that energy can exist in finite packets only and not in quantities of arbitrary amount. These relations have led to the invention of the most revolutionary of human ideas, for the quantum theory is different in kind from any invented before. The theory of relativity was really only a refinement of previous theories, and is not generically different from them. The quantum theory was invented by Planck, who consequently may be considered the most revolutionary of all human thinkers.

If the temperature of the surface of a star is known, the rate at which the surface radiates energy in the form of heat and light may be calculated. This result will reveal how much light is leaving each square inch of the star's surface, i.e., the candle-power per square inch. By observing the star's apparent total candle-power, and hence, if its distance is known, deriving its actual candle-power, the area of its surface is easily found by dividing the total actual candle-power by the candle-power per unit area determined from the colour study. From the surface the diameter can easily be deduced.

Diameters of stars determined in this way agree well with the results obtained directly by the interferometer method described in the last section. The remarkable mutual confirmation of the two so distinct methods is a proof of their correctness, and an inspiration of confidence in both experiment and theory.

A study of the light-rays from stars can reveal the density of the stellar material. The rays constituting the light-bundle which we ordinarily see, the jumble of rays arriving all mixed up from the star, have varying characteristics when separated out. For instance, the ray of hydrogen-light from one star may correspond exactly in wave-size with the similar ray from another star, but be better defined, sharper in its definition.

What may this mean? Not improbably that the well-
defined hydrogen rays were emitted by hydrogen atoms
under less distracted conditions, that the atoms were
being less jostled about while emitting the hydrogen
light in the first than in the second star. If the atoms
in the first star were being less jostled than those in the
second, presumably there were fewer of them about,
and hence the gas was less dense. The density of the
gas emitting the light can be calculated from the sharp-
ness of the rays into which the light is analysed by the
spectroscope.

The average density of a star may be calculated if
the weight and diameter are known. The results by
both methods again confirm each other, to the pleasure
of astronomers.

The table gives some particulars of the candle- or
sun-power, surface temperature, weight, diameter, colour,
density of some well-known stars.

Bright-ness.	Star.	Colour.	Surface Temp.	W'ght.	Density	Diam-eter.
1	Sun . .	Yellow	6,000° C.	1	1·41	1
1,200	Betelgeuse .	Red	3,100	15	6×10^{-7}	290
100	Arcturus .	Orange	4,300	8	·0003	27
80,000	Canopus .	White	11,000	100	·0001	·100
18,000	Rigel . .	Bluish	16,000	60	·002	30
26	Sirius . .	White	11,000	2·4	·42	1·8
·003	Dark compan-ion of Sirius	White	7,500	0·96	27,000	·034
3,400	Antares .	Red	3,100	30	3×10^{-7}	450

The large red stars Antares and Betelgeuse are
extremely tenuous, on the average a millionth the
density of water. They are glowing rarefied gas, similar
to the contents of the neon tubes used in advertising.

Even Canopus, which shines 80,000 times as powerfully as the Sun, is on the average 10,000 times less
dense than water. The very bright stars are very
tenuous, and their powerful shining is due to their

great area. Canopus could contain the whole orbit of Venus. No wonder such a star has 80,000 times the candle-power of the Sun.

Compared with the greatest stars, the Sun is quite small, and indeed is a dwarf among its kind. We have no particular reason to be proud of the Sun on account of its size.

With one exception, the brightness of the stars in the table increases with their weight: a heavy star is bright. This remarkable relation has been explained theoretically by Eddington. The exception is extraordinary. Apparently the companion of Sirius has a density 27,000 times that of water ! How ? That has been explained, too. A star discovered by Van Maanen has a density 400,000 times that of water. How ? The answer is simple. Atoms are usually bulky objects for their weight. They consist of a speck of a nucleus surrounded by rings of electrons, the rings being of great radius compared with that of the nuclear speck. Under the very high temperature and pressure in certain stars, they loose their rings of electrons so the nuclear particles all pack enormously closer together, making the stellar material very dense. Matter 400,000 times as dense as water is one of the simplest things to understand.

A new theory of the constitution of the stars has been advanced recently by E. A. Milne. He has found a new solution of the mathematical equations which describe the state of a star. According to his solution, the centres of stars are extremely dense, about 50,000, or even a million, times that of water, while the outer parts are rare. There is a very steep decline of temperature and density from the centre of the star outwards. In his view, the centres of stars, and of the Sun, are at billions of degrees Centigrade, i.e., at temperatures of the order 1,000,000,000,000° C. All stars, or nearly all, must be regarded as containing a "white dwarf" in the middle. On the older theory of Eddington stars were supposed to be fairly uniform in density throughout: the decline from the centre to the surface was gradual. Under this theory the origin of the immense energy of the stars was obscure, for they radiate energy in prodigious quantities which can arise only from the annihilation of matter, the transfer of matter into energy, and yet the conditions in stars did not seem to be severe enough to cause energy to be liberated from matter. With the immense temperatures required by Milne's theory the change of matter into energy is quite reasonable, for there is no difficulty in supposing that the matter in the centre of a star roasted at a temperature of perhaps a billion degrees will dissolve into energy in the form of radiation. The existence of a solid or liquid core to nearly all stars also helps to explain the splitting of stars into twins. Jeans demanded such cores to stars partly for that reason, since an entirely gaseous star is incapable of splitting into twin stars under the influence of rotatory forces only, but a star with a liquid or solid core might. Another consequence of the very high central temperatures of stars according to Milne's theory is that though the temperature is enormous the material behaves as if it were frozen. In this extreme condition the atoms in the material of the star's centre are degenerated and cannot radiate. The explanation involves an application of the quantum theory, and the result is that the material is at such an extremely high temperature that it is incapacitated from radiating because all the electrons its atoms would use in radiating have been torn off, so to an observer would appear nearly absolutely cold.

The recent experimental researches of Professor Simon of Berlin on the effects of high pressure on the change of state from liquid to solid have special interest in connection with the problem of the condition of matter in the centres of stars and celestial bodies. He has shown that helium may be kept solid at temperatures 40° C. above its ordinary melting point, if subjected to pressures of several tons to the square inch. He believes substances will remain solid at any temperature if the pressure is high enough. At the enormous pressures in the centre of the Earth, and still more at the centres of stars, matter may be solid in spite of the huge temperatures. The known solidity of the Earth's centre would be explained by his suggestion, and the theoretically desirable solidity of the centres of stars, which would enable them to split into twins under sufficient centrifugal forces, would be established to be more probable.

VII

VARIABLE STARS

We have all heard that the stars do not really twinkle, and that their one obvious sign of activity is an appearance due to variations in the light-bending quality of the air through which they are seen. Not only were the stars immutable, they were constant also, in every way eternal, we used to hear. We have now learnt that the stars are comparatively uniform in weight, hustle through space at enormous speeds and vary immensely in size. That certain stars vary in brightness has been mentioned; in particular, stars like δ Cephei and the Pole Star, and that this type of star has enabled the depths of space to be explored.

At least some stars are variable. In fact, 5,000 are known to be, and five per cent. of all the stars are suspected of being variable in brightness. Besides hurtling through space, five per cent. of the stars actually vary their apparent candle-power.

The variation in about half of the cases is due to the mutual eclipsing of twin stars, which has been described. This variability is not due to the stars themselves, but to accidents of place and time.

PLATE II

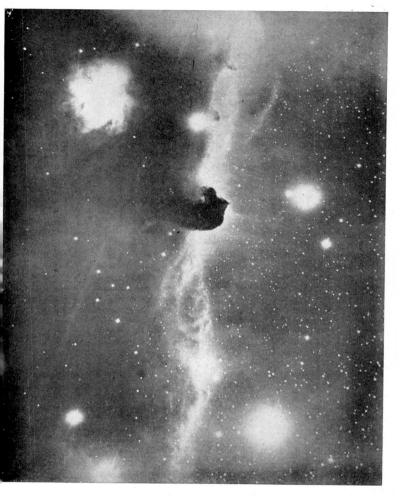

(Mount Wilson.)

The Horse's Head Nebula ; a dark nebula obscuring light from beyond it.

See page 28.

PLATE III

The Globular Cluster of stars in Hercules.   (*Plaskett.*

See page 28.

PLATE IV

N. C. G. 3587. (*Ritchey*.)
The Owl Nebula: a gaseous nebula with a star in the middle.

See page 43.

PLATE V

(*Mount Wilson.*)

N. G. C. 7217.

Island Universe presented broadside.

See page 33.

PLATE VI

(*Mount Wilson.*)

N. G. C. 4594.
Island Universe presented edge-on.
See page 33.

PLATE VII

Nebulosity in the Pleiades. (*Roberts.*

See page 43.

PLATE VIII

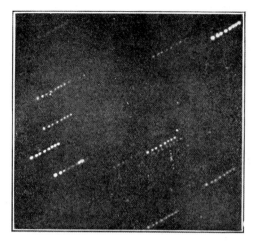

(*Harvard.*)

In the bottom left hand corner U Cephei is shown varying in brightness in a series of exposures on the same plate.

See page 51.

PLATE IX

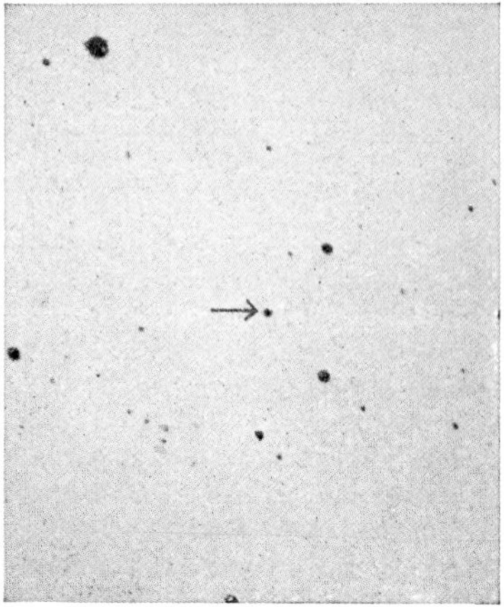

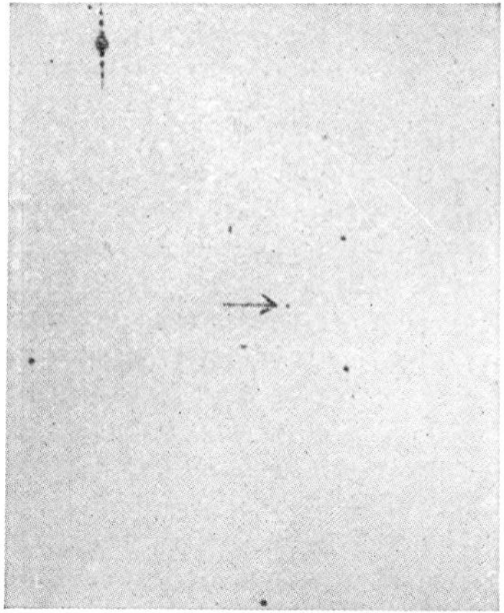

June 3rd, 1918.

May 22, 1888.

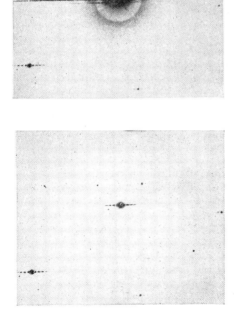

June 7th, 1918. June 8th, 1918.

The sudden blazing up of Nova Aquilae in June, 1918.

(*Harvard Circular* 210.)

See page 63.

PLATE X

(*Barnard.*)

The corona of the Sun during a total eclipse at sun-spot minimum, May 28th, 1900.

PLATE XI

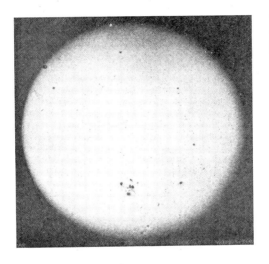

(*Yerkes.*)

Spots on the Sun at sun-spot maximum.
See page 67.

PLATE XII

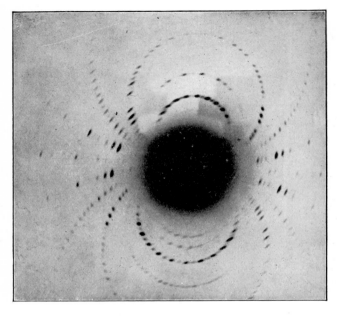

(*Bragg.*)

X-ray photograph of Nickel Sulphate crystal.

See page 93.

PLATE XIII

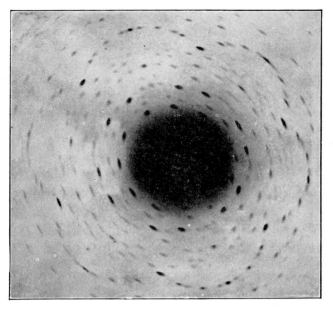

(*Bragg.*)

X-ray photograph of Beryl crystal.

See page 93.

Further Plates between pages 128-129, and in Volume Two.

still obscure. Eddington has explained many of their features on the assumption that once the pulsation has started, it keeps up steadily because the star is elastic in volume under the influence of gravitational light-pressure and variations of pressure due to temperature changes. Why the pulsations should ever start is not known.

Jeans' theory is entirely different. He considers the pulsations are due to a star's tending to split into two under the influence of its own centrifugal forces. The star's rate of rotation has increased until its figure has become unstable, and commences to bulge out into two knobs swaying away and towards each other,

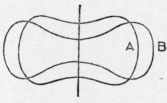

Fig. 14.

the star continuing to revolve round the vertical axis as its surface sways back and forth from A to B. The latter change would correspond to the surface movements observed on Cepheids. Jeans' theory will also help to explain peculiar variations ascribable to the difference in luminosity of the star as it changes through its odd dumb-bell shapes, combined with the different aspects due to rotation. For instance, when the dumb-bells are end on the area of the star will be either that of circle A or of circle B, or some intermediate area (fig. 15).

Mathematical investigation shows that only liquid bodies can assume more or less stable dumb-bell shapes. Jeans has to assume the stars are liquid-like,

c

or have liquid-like cores. He has given some good reasons for supposing such liquid-like substances could exist, though many physicists do not accept them. Eddington believes the stars are perfect gases, and on his assumptions the liquid-star theory is incorrect. Are stars gas or partly liquid? That is the question. The answer is undecided.

Apart from theories, the most astonishing facts are known about Cepheids. Mere comparison for the Cepheids whose distances are known has shown that there is a very close relation between the period and the candle-power.

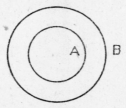

FIG. 15.

If the period of a Cepheid is known, its candle-power may be written down. If the apparent candle-power is compared with the actual, the distance of the Cepheid is known, and also of its neighbours.

The explanation of the marvellous connection is entirely obscure. Besides this extraordinary fact, Cepheids turn out to be very bright stars, of the order ten thousand times as bright as the Sun. Thus the brightest of stars turn out to be some of the most revealing. If Cepheids were feeble in light they would tell us enormously less than they do about the extent of space. The combination of great brightness with the precise connection between period and candle-power is one of the happiest facts of astronomy.

VIII

THE SUN

DARK spots occasionally appear on the Sun. The number of sunspots varies fairly regularly, rising to a maximum about every eleven years.

At the beginning of an eleven-year period, the spots begin to appear in high latitudes on the Sun and gradually break out nearer and nearer the equator as the years pass. About the eleventh year they appear on the Sun's equator, and simultaneously spots again break out in the higher latitudes as the harbinger of the new cycle. Sunspots appear to be due to some internal commotion which starts in a high latitude of the Sun's surface, and slowly works down to its equator (Plate XI).

This eleven-year period of disturbance in the Sun manifests itself in other ways. When the Sun is totally eclipsed by the Moon the shape of the corona, the exceedingly rare envelope of gas extending half a million miles from the Sun's surface, can be seen.

The shape of the corona at sunspot maximum differs from that at sunspot minimum. The corona varies its shape in eleven-year periods.

At maximum it is equally radiated in all directions. At minimum it appears rather as a pair of whiskers on the Sun's equator, with wisps of hair on the North and South Poles (Plate X).

The eleven-year variations in the Sun's condition are manifested by effects observable on the Earth. Magnetic storms which affect compasses are known to appear on the Earth when spots are evident on the Sun.

The frequency of aurorae is closely related to the sunspot period.

There is evidence that the Earth's average surface temperature is lower by about three-quarters of a degree when sunspots are most numerous. Measurement shows there is also probably an eleven-year variation in the rate at which the Sun radiates heat and light.

These facts suggest the Sun is a slightly variable star. Instead of varying over a period of upwards of a thousand days, like the long-period variable stars, it varies very slightly in a period of eleven years.

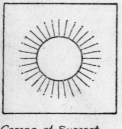
Corona at Sunspot maximum

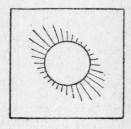
at Sunspot minimum

Fig. 16.

The slow and slight variation suggests the Sun is an aged variable star which has become leisurely and feeble after aeons of pulsation.

Though there are slight variations in the Sun's state, it remains on the whole very stable. A consideration of the fact that it is stable gives insight into the condition of its interior.

The Sun's surface temperature is about 6,000° Centigrade, and it must be hotter inside because heat and light are continually being radiated away from it. At these high temperatures all substances are gaseous, at least, if they are on the Earth. There is a strong presumption they are gaseous on the Sun. The Sun is an enormous globe of gas. The gas in the centre will be enormously compressed because it will have to support columns of gas nearly half a million miles high. If a football could exist at the centre of the Sun, it would have to be pumped to a pressure of six million tons to the square inch to stay up.

The pressure of the gas in a football or motor-tyre does not depend on the number of molecules only, or quantity of gas inside. As everyone knows, footballs and motor-tyres should not be left standing in hot sunshine because the heat increases the pressure of the air inside. The pressure also depends on the temperature. If the temperature is high, less gas is needed to make the football or tyre hard. It is the same with the Sun and other stars. The enormous pressures at the centre of the Sun are supported by quite small quantities of gas because the temperature is enormous. If the temperature were not enormous, the Sun would contain far more gas and consequently weigh much more than it is known to.

Calculation suggests the gas at the Sun's centre is only about thirty times as dense as water, and the comparatively small number of gas molecules needed per unit volume to make up that low density could support the pressure of 6,000,000 tons to the square inch only because it is at the great temperature of 40,000,000° C. There is nothing surprising about high temperatures. They merely mean that the particles of gas are moving at huge speeds. For instance, the a-particles shot out from radium travel at 10,000 miles a second. If a gas of flying a-particles could be collected, its temperature would be 50,000,000,000° C. Fortunately a-particles do not burn us because there are so few of them ever together, but it is as well to know that every radium-painted wrist-watch contains some matter at a temperature of 50,000,000,000° C. because the 40,000,000° C. at the centre of the Sun is a trifle in comparison. Whereas the gas particles in the air travel at 500 yards a second, those at the Sun's centre travel at 100 miles a second, only 300 or 400 times faster.

The matter at the Sun's centre is shining much more brightly than that at the surface because it is so much hotter.

When light falls on an object it presses it. The pressure is very small for ordinary light. The brighter the light the greater the pressure. The very bright light from the intensely hot matter at the Sun's centre actually presses upwards with a pressure of some hundreds of thousands of tons to the square inch. In fact, quite an appreciable portion of the weight of the Sun's matter pressing towards the centre is borne by mere insubstantial waves of radiation. The internal light of the Sun is not of the same wave-length as visible light, but similar rather to that of X-rays used in hospitals.

Matter bombarded by X-rays which themselves exert a pressure on it of hundreds of thousands of tons to the square inch, and roasted to a temperature of 40,000,000° C., is thoroughly reduced.

The atoms are broken down to a fraction of their normal terrestrial size, and take up much less space. For this reason, the matter can still go on behaving like a gas even if its density is thirty times that of water.

Another curious quality of gas in this battered condition is its opacity: the internal gas of the Sun is extraordinarily opaque, quite unlike the translucent air of the Earth's atmosphere. The remarkably sharp edge of the Sun's disc is a proof of this fact. Within a distance of 50 miles the Sun's surface changes from great transparency to opacity. Fifty miles is only one ten-thousandth of the Sun's radius, so the Sun's figure is as accurate as that of a ball-bearing.

Radiations are a form of energy possessing weight. This property of radiation enables it to exert pressure on the bodies it strikes. Anything that radiates is losing energy, and consequently weight. A red-hot poker, a candle, the Sun, loses weight merely by radiating heat and light. Feeble radiators such as candles lose extremely little weight by radiation, but they do lose some. Powerful radiators such as the Sun lose appreciable weights merely by shining. The Sun loses 300,000,000 tons by weight every minute. Though the Sun has been doing this for millions of years, its weight and power have not decreased much during an immense period of time. If the Sun had been much heavier and hotter a few hundred million years ago than it is now, the evolution of life on the Earth could not have happened. The Earth's surface could not have been cool enough. The very fact that the Earth's surface temperature has remained within the narrow limit between which life as we know it exists proves that the Sun has not greatly changed in shining power for hundreds of millions of years. Yet it is losing light and weight at the rate of 300,000,000 tons a minute. This proves the hugeness of the Sun.

Nevertheless, this loss of weight by radiating enables an upper limit to be fixed to the age of the Sun.

That stars are remarkably uniform in weight has been mentioned, the heaviest being not more than about 100 times the Sun's weight. This is an observed fact, and there are theories which show that stars of larger mass would be unstable. There is evidence that the Sun could never have been more than 100 times as weighty as it is now. Yet it loses weight at the rate of 300,000,000 tons a minute.

The age of the Sun can easily be calculated if it has always lost weight at that rate and was never more than 100 times heavier than it is now. It would be 130 billion years. As it probably radiated enormously more powerfully when it was new, it is probably not more than 5 billion years old.

What has the Sun to look forward to ? Suppose it continues to radiate until it weighs no more than a faint white dwarf such as Krueger 60 ? Its rate of radiation will decrease steadily, and it will not decline into the senility of Krueger 60 until five hundred million million years have passed. After all that time the Sun will still be not negligible, and will probably continue though in that enfeebled condition for even more aeons of time, until some accident or contrary rhythm in the universe redirects the tendency of its existence.

IX

THE PLANETS

JEANS' THEORY

SOME thousand million years ago, a star and the Sun passed by each other. The star was larger than the Sun, so that when they drew near the Sun suffered most from the mutual pull they exerted on each other owing to gravitation. Presently they became so close that their mutual pulls produced more than distortion, the gravitational pulls raised large tides as high as mountains on each star, but the tides on the Sun were the higher, because the Sun was the smaller star. As they approached still more closely the tide on the Sun grew so high that the wave reached up the Sun's sky and began to stream right out into space, towards the greater star.

When the star attained its shortest distance from the Sun, the gigantic tide of streaming matter reached its maximum, and as the star passed on, leaving the Sun behind, the amount of matter leaving the Sun as the height of a super-high-tide gradually decreased, until presently the great star no longer raised more than a large bump on the Sun, and ultimately wandered away too far to raise even that. The stages in the process are represented in fig. 17.

Thus the Sun was left with a cigar-shaped filament of gas torn out of it. The gas tended to concentrate into masses under its own gravitation, as in fig. 18.

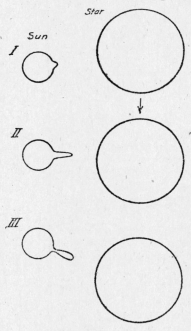

FIG. 17 (after Jeans).

The large condensations in the centre formed vast masses of slowly cooling gas and remained gaseous long after the smaller masses solidified.

Such a situation very well describes the solar system. The various planets are at fairly regular distances from

the Sun and the great planets Jupiter and Saturn are of
low density and still largely gaseous. There is one gap,
corresponding to a planet which would occupy the
orbit of the asteroids, the swarm of tiny planets up to
a few hundred miles in diameter which revolve round
the Sun between the orbits of Mars and Jupiter. Perhaps these could be regarded as one planet if gathered
together into a bunch.

As the cigar-shaped filament cooled into separate
masses, the planets, these moved about in irregular
orbits, since the filament could not have been expected
to condense into perfectly regularly moving masses.
Some started with a slant in one direction, others in
another, due to a twist given them by the greater star

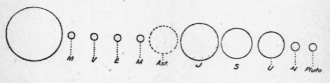

FIG. 18.

before it had left the Sun's vicinity. So the planets
commenced their circulatory life with very irregular
paths, moving in ellipses which brought them occasionally very close to the Sun and to each other.

When this happened, and one of the planets approached
very near the Sun, the Sun did to the planet what it had
suffered from the great star. A filament was pulled out
of the planet to condense in parts in its turn. Thus the
numerous satellites of Jupiter, Saturn and Uranus were
born.

At this period the solar system was decidedly in the
rough. Planets were pursuing irregular courses, there
were many odd bits of matter left lying about, not incor-
porated in the planets during the great initial condensation. The planets ploughed their ways through

these clouds of débris, gradually collecting most of it into themselves and increasing their own bulk, after the style of the planetesimal theory of Chamberlain and Moulton. This ploughing through and collecting of the débris rubbed the corners off the planets' irregular orbits and caused them to move in more and more circular ones. But this trimming had not proceeded far enough to prevent the planet between Mars and Jupiter repeatedly approaching too near to Jupiter. It must have swung within a distance less than 2·45 times Jupiter's radius. Why? Because the tidal forces on a planet, even if it is solid, are so great when it is revolving within that distance of Jupiter that it flies to bits. The planet between Mars and Jupiter was whole once, but approached so near Jupiter that it was disrupted into a swarm of small bodies, the asteroids. These still continue about their parent's orbit to-day.

There is another example of disruption through too close approach. Saturn's nearest moon sank within the 2·45 limit ages ago, and was torn to pieces and has spread its dust in rings round Saturn.

The same fate awaits the Moon. It will end as a ring of dust around the Earth. The Moon is steadily receding from the Earth at present owing to the slowing of the Earth's rate of rotation by tidal friction. Each time the tide flows up the Thames or the Behring Strait, the Earth's rate of rotation, and hence its angular momentum, is reduced.

In a self-contained system like the Earth and Moon, if angular momentum is taken from one part of it, it must be transferred to another. The angular momentum of the Earth is transferred through the agency of the tides to the momentum of the Moon revolving round the Earth. The Moon drops away, so that the leverage round the Earth, as it were, is increased.

After an immense age, the Earth's rotation will be reduced to the same period as that of the rotation of the Moon round it; i.e., the day and the month will become equal. The Earth will always present the same face to the Moon, as the Moon now always offers the same face to the Earth, and the period of the day and the month will be about forty-seven of our present days. Though the mutual tidal forces of the Earth and Moon will be quits, the Sun's tidal forces on the Earth will still act. These will further slow down the Earth's rotation, and make the day longer than the month. The friction of the tides on the Earth due to the Moon will tend to increase the day by preventing it decreasing, and consequently will entail a decrease in the angular momentum of the Moon, so the Moon will gradually approach the Earth once more. After an incredible age, when perhaps the Sun has burnt itself down to a feeble star, the Moon will approach to within 12,000 miles of the Earth, into the dangerous zone. The tidal forces of the Earth will disrupt the Moon's solid bulk into fragments, and the earth thenceforth will have no Moon, but a dusty ring of débris, a celestial wraith.

A much earlier fate awaits one member of the solar system. The orbit of the innermost satellite of Jupiter is only 2·54 times Jupiter's radius. It has to contract only from 2·54 to 1·45 times Jupiter's radius, and then it will be burst into bits, and Jupiter will thenceforth appear in the sky with a ring and only eight moons.

X

THE CONDITION OF THE PLANETS

MERCURY is nearest the Sun. It probably has no atmosphere, since it is too small in mass to prevent gases from escaping into space. The surface temperature of the sunlit side has been estimated by measuring the intensity of the heat coming from it, and appears to be about 350° C., which is hot enough to melt lead. The surface reflects exceptionally little of the light falling on it from the Sun, which suggests it is rocky and uneven, and not the top of an atmosphere. The Sun's tidal effect has reduced Mercury to showing always the same face to the Sun, so the planet's day is equal to its year, i.e., about 88 days.

The next nearest planet is Venus. Its surface appears very smooth, as if it were the outside of a swathe of clouds. Faint markings have been observed, but not distinctly.

The planet's day appears to be a long one, certainly longer than twenty of ours, but probably not as much

FIG. 19.

as its year of seven and a half months. It probably does not continuously show the same face to the Sun. Pettit and Nicholson have shown that the dark side of Venus is fairly warm, about—25° C., and it could not be warm unless it faced the Sun fairly frequently. Venus definitely has an atmosphere. When it appears to us as a thin crescent, the hours are prolonged owing to the extension of the atmosphere. Spectroscopic examination shows the higher atmosphere is almost devoid of oxygen, and has little water-vapour. This fact suggests there is not much oxygen in its lower atmosphere, and consequently no life. Oxygen is an active element and possibly could not exist freely in an atmosphere unless it were breathed into it, as plants breathe oxygen into the Earth's atmosphere. Indeed, it has been suggested that the oxygen in the Earth's atmosphere is entirely due to plants in the past and present, the plants of the coal measures, for instance, which liberated vast quantities of oxygen into the atmosphere.

The next planet is the Earth. H. N. Russell has interestingly summarized the possible appearance of the Earth from other planets. To an observer on the Moon, it would appear at full earth forty times as bright as full moon to us, with fleecy areas of cloud over a blue ground. From Venus, the Earth would appear at its brightest six times as bright as Venus at its brightest appears to us. The Moon would look about as bright as Jupiter, and would appear very close to the Earth: the two would be twin planets and the most remarkable celestial objects in Venus' sky. The Earth would appear bluish, and the Moon yellowish. As cloud reflects about three times as strongly as land, the Earth would have a total of about half its surface covered with white patches. Circular patches of cloud would mark the existence of cyclonic storms. The surface would appear blue for the same reason that mountains look blue. The reflection of sunlight from the oceans would be very brilliant, forests a dull blue, cultivated regions and steppes a lighter colour.

A being on the Moon provided with a powerful telescope would learn much about the Earth's surface at the rare times when free from cloud. Coastline would be conspicuous, mountains would be detected by their shadows, seasons easily deduced, and the extension of the snow-line in winter.

Observers on Venus would be able to see objects fifty miles in diameter.

The Moon observers could detect cities smoking by day, and shining by night, though they would not be able to distinguish them from volcanoes; the clearing of the forests during periods of years in America, and perhaps the great lake made by the Gatun Dam on the Panama Canal. They would probably not feel sure of ascribing these appearances to human or intelligent endeavour.

After the Earth, Mars. It is much smaller than the Earth, being 4,215 miles in diameter. A body weighing 100 lb. on the Earth would weigh 38 lb. on Mars. When at its closest to the Earth, it presents a ruddy disc. Its reflecting power is equal to that of fairly dark-coloured rocks, and its surface is relatively smooth. Its spots enable its day to be measured very exactly, and the length is 24 h. 37 m. 22.58 secs. There are polar caps of snow probably not more than 6 feet thick, and evidence of seasons. The red areas are probably earthy, the seasonal changes in appearance being due perhaps to soaking with melted snow from the atmosphere. Fine wisp-like marks or scratches are sometimes seen; these are the celebrated "canals". The exact evidence of their nature is not proportional to the speculations they have inspired. Comparatively nothing is certainly known about these alleged "canals".

Mars has an atmosphere less dense than the Earth's. Clouds have occasionally been seen in it. The oxygen is 15 per cent. and the water-vapour 5 per cent. of that normally in the Earth's atmosphere.

In the equatorial regions the temperature rises to about 10° C. at noon, and the polar caps are at about —70° C. Mars is quite a chilly planet, having very cold nights with many degrees of frost.

Some of the darkest areas may be vegetation: the existence of oxygen in Mars' atmosphere is evidence for the existence of vegetation. Pickering has suggested the "canals" may be vegetation growing along rift valleys after the soil has been soaked by spring melted snow, as the Nile would appear to a Moon observer as a streak of green on the yellow African desert.

Mars has two tiny satellites: Phobos only 10 miles in diameter, and Deimos even smaller, about 5 miles in diameter. These are little more than large stones whizzing round their primary. Phobos completes a revolution in 7 h. 39 m., and Deimos in 30 h. 18 m. Thus Phobos travels right across Mars' sky twice every day, rising in the west and setting in the east, because it is always overtaking its primary, which rotates only once in 24 hours.

The oxygen in Mars' atmosphere suggests there is life of some sort on the planet, plant life at least. The severe climate would kill all but the lowest forms of animal life known to us. The evidence for any more complicated forms of life such as that of man is very doubtful.

After Mars come the remains of the planet that Jupiter smashed. The largest is Ceres, 480 miles in diameter. It is probably a rough chunk of rock of rather irregular shape. Its gravity is so small that the bullet from a modern rifle fired vertically from the surface would leave Ceres for ever. If all the asteroids were lumped together they probably would not weigh more than $\frac{1}{1,000}$ or $\frac{1}{500}$ the Earth's weight.

Eros is remarkable for providing the most accurate data for the Sun's distance from the Earth. Occasionally it approaches very near to the Earth, one occasion being in 1931, when it was only 16,200,000 miles away on January 30th. The extensive observations made will probably re-settle the measure of the Sun's distance considerably more accurately than ever before.

When the Asteroids began to be discovered, all sorts of fantastic names were given them, mythological until existing lore was almost exhausted, then names after "cities, colleges, and friends of their discoverers,

ocean steamers, pet dogs, and favourite desserts !"
Presently, each was given a number, and the habits
of garden suburbs withheld from invading celestial
regions.

After the Asteroids, Jupiter. This huge planet is
88,640 miles in diameter at the Equator. Its density
is about the same as that of the Sun, 1·34 times that of
water. It rotates more quickly than any other planet,
in about 9 h. 53 m. The surface speed at the equator
is consequently very high. Small differences in rate of
rotation of points at ranging latitudes indicate enormous
currents in the planet's atmosphere travelling up
to 200 miles per hour. The high rate of rotation
causes the planet to be distinctly flattened at the
poles.

Measurement of its outer surface temperature registers
—140° C. This upsets the old idea that Jupiter is a
mass of very hot gas. Indeed, the clouds on the surface
must be due not to smoke, as it were, but to particles
of solid carbon dioxide or other gases with very low
liquefying and solidifying points. Jeffreys has suggested
that Jupiter has a heavy iron or metallic core,
with great layers of ice around it, and then a huge
atmosphere of very cold gas.

There is evidence from the irregularity in the eclipses
of the satellites by Jupiter that the planet's surface is
uneven, clouds sometimes varying upwards of 100 miles
in height from the average surface.

Saturn's condition resembles Jupiter's; it is only
0·715 times the density of water. It has been observed
to rotate equatorially once in 10 h. 14 m. 24 secs. and
10·38 m. in a higher latitude. The equatorial diameter
is 74,100 miles, so the centrifugal force at the Equator
is very great, no less than 0·17 of the gravitational
force. Any body on the equator of Saturn loses a
sixth of its weight merely by virtue of being whirled
around by the planet.

Its surface temperature is—150° C. This is 30° C.

higher than the temperature the Sun's rays would raise
it. Jeffreys has suggested it also has a metallic core
sheathed in ice and an atmosphere filled with something like clouds of solid carbon dioxide particles.
He suggests the 30° C. excess temperature is due to
radioactive material in the surface layers.

Uranus is 1·27 times as dense as water. It is another
of the large cold gassy planets. Its day is about $10\frac{3}{4}$
hours, and its surface is colder than Saturn's, about
—180° C. Neptune is of the same type, 1·6 times as
dense as water, with a surface temperature probably less
than—200° C. As for the new planet, Pluto, its surface
temperature must be not more than 30 or 40 degrees
from absolute zero, say — 240° C.

Though these temperatures are exceedingly low,
there is evidence the major planetary atmospheres
contain some water-vapour, according to experiments
by Prof. McLennan. How water-vapour could exist
in any quantity at these very low temperatures is
mysterious. The modern conception of the major
planets has changed from one of fiery to one of cold
turbulence, from the condition of Dante's red-hot
"city which has Dis to name" to that of his icy floor
of Hell exactly at the centre of the Earth, where "The
Emperor of the realm of woe issued by half the breast
forth out of the ice;" . . .

XI

PLUTO

SINCE the planet Neptune was discovered eighty-four
years ago indirectly through calculations based on

irregularities in the movement of Uranus astronomers
have speculated on the possibility of the existence of
planets beyond even Neptune. The most exhaustive
calculations were made by the late Percival Lowell, a
distinguished American astronomer and founder of the
observatory at Flagstaff, Arizona, and published in
1914. Much time was given to the search for this pre-
dicted planet by the staff of this observatory, and the
search continued after Lowell's death. On January
21st, 1930, Tombaugh, a young assistant, noticed an
object in the predicted part of the sky that seemed to
move like a planet, in spite of its very small magnitude,
which was as low as 15·5. Later Lampland and E. C.
Slipher followed it photographically and visually and
after some weeks' observation were convinced it was
the planet for which the search had been made (see
Plate I). Since then it has been observed regularly from
observatories in many parts of the world, and a search
of old photographic plates has revealed that pictures
of it were taken unwittingly in 1919 and at other times.
From the data collected, the details of the planet's
characteristics have been calculated. The figures pre-
dicted by Lowell and one of the observed sets of figures
compare as follows:

	Predicted.	Actual.
Period of revolution . .	282 years	249·17 years
Eccentricity of orbit . .	0·202	0·254
Longitude of perihelion .	205°	212° 30′
Perihelion passage . .	In year, 1991.2	In year, 1989.16
Inclination of orbit . .	10°	17° 9′

Considering the slight perturbations in Neptune upon
which Lowell had to develop his calculations, the
agreement is remarkable. But while much in the pre-
dicted and actual observations is close there are some
large discrepancies. Lowell estimated the new planet

would be six times as massive as the Earth, and probably therefore much larger in diameter. The larger diameter would give the planet considerable reflective power so it would appear as bright as magnitude 13 or so. In fact, it is observed to be of magnitude 15·5, i.e., about six times less bright than predicted. It is not very easy to see how a planet of such low luminosity could be larger than the Earth or indeed much larger than the Moon. For it to have the perturbing effect noticed in Neptune it would have to be considerably more massive than the Earth, indeed six times as massive. If the planet, which has been named Pluto, is both smaller than the Earth, and six times as massive it must be twenty or so times as dense as water, which makes one wonder what it is made of, for in that case it would be fifty or a hundred times denser than water, and material of that density is quite unknown at the low temperatures of planets. If Pluto were no denser than the Earth, its effect on Neptune would be too small to be observed. The mass of Pluto is therefore a very interesting subject of investigation.

The orbit of Pluto is exceptionally elliptical; though Pluto is usually far beyond Neptune's orbit it is actually inside at its nearest approach to the Sun. The two planets run no risk of collision because Pluto's orbit is heavily inclined from Neptune's, but at certain epochs they pass very close to each other.

H. N. Russell states that, on certain assumptions, Pluto and Neptune were at their closest in 976 B.C. and will be again in A.D. 9238. At these conjunctions the two planets are relatively closer than the closest conjunctions of any other pair of planets in the solar system, i.e., that of the Earth and Venus. In 1892 the planets were comparatively close and will be again in 1965, so in 35 years' time astronomers will have specially good opportunities for observing the inter-reactions of mass between Neptune and Pluto, from which the mass of Pluto can be calculated. It is interesting to note

that the average distance of Pluto from the Sun is
39·60 units (the unit is the distance from Earth to Sun),
which roughly agrees with the figure Bode's law postu-
lates for Neptune. At its nearest Pluto is 29·55 units
and at its farthest 49·7 units from the Sun, the least
distance of Neptune being 29·82. The exceptional
ellipticity of Pluto's orbit suggests speculations about
its origin. Was Pluto evolved from the Sun at the same
time as the other planets, or was it captured by the
Sun as it strayed through space? Are there yet more
planets to be found beyond Pluto? Future research
may decide these questions.

XII

THE EARTH

THE Earth is substantially solid, though it may be
slightly honeycombed in parts, the interstices of which
are filled with hot liquid or plastic material. It has a
large core probably made of iron and nickel, in fact
natural nickel-steel. Around this core there is a deep
layer of basaltic rock, a thousand or so miles thick.
Plastered on to the top of this layer are sundry thin
areas of granite rock, and in the spaces between these
areas the basalt surface is covered with water. Fig. 20
indicates these divisions exaggeratedly.

The proper reference surface for the boundary
of the Earth is seen to be the ocean bed. The continents
are merely films of lighter material let into this surface,
while the oceans are a watery covering of those parts
not covered by the continents. This conception of the
Earth's structure is derived from several lines of research.
The study of the way earthquake waves pass through
the Earth shows that the interior is solid and also has
a boundary about 1,500 miles below the surface.

The density of the Earth is 5·5 times that of water; hence it must have a lot of heavy material inside, as the rock on the surface is on the average only 2·7 times that of water. The Earth is also a magnet: this suggests the heavy material is iron. Besides, materials coming from outer space are often iron, and these may very probably have originated from the same sources as the Earth. Material coming up from the depths in volcanic eruptions is always basalt, a heavy rock about three times the density of water. The sequence of densities is reasonable, 5·5 in the centre, 3·0 in the middle layer,

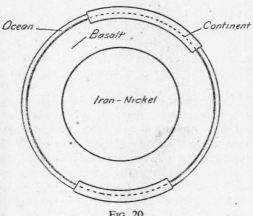

FIG. 20.

2·7 in the superficial continental rocks, and 1·0 in the oceans.

The continental "flakes" have the remarkable property of behaving as if they floated in the basalt layer. On the average there is about enough sticking above the basalt surface to hold the amount below beneath the surface, on the iceberg principle. This is a strong argument that the basalt has been liquid and the continents were scum floating on the top. When the basalt solidi-

fied the scum was gripped tight. At their thickest the
continents measure about 30 miles. In the Himalayas
there is an average thickness of 3 miles above the ocean
level and 24 or so miles below. This fact is known
from gravitational survey. The mass of the Himalayas
does not increase the gravitational attraction on matter
as much as is expected. By measuring the deficiency,
the depth of material of low density may be calculated
to be about thirty miles. These general features of the
Earth are what might be expected. When the matter
was pulled out of the Sun at the birth of the solar
system, it was gaseous. The heavy metals and rocks

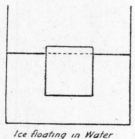

Ice floating in Water

FIG. 21.

liquefied first and the dense metals sank into the interior.
The light very refractory rocks solidified first and floated
on the liquid rocks as slag. Later the liquid rocks
solidified and gripped the previously floating slag and
made it into continents. Still later the water-vapour
liquefied and filled the spaces between the continents
to form the oceans.

Land as we know it, the scum of Earth, is of the
order 30 miles thick. That is about 40,000 feet. Geolo-
gists have detected remnants of strata which, if all
added together, make 500,000 feet. 500,000 into 40,000
won't go. The answer is that in making its strata the
Earth has used the same material over and over again,

often not using up all the leavings from the time before. We arrive at once at the suggestion that the Earth has periods of stratum-manufacture.

The Earth contains radium and other radioactive substances. As these disintegrate, the particles they fling out strike their surroundings, and raise the temperature as their energy of motion is changed into heat. These substances are perpetually raising the temperature of the Earth, especially below the continents, which act as blankets and retain the heat. Under the oceans the heat will soon leak away, for the waters are moving continually and cool the rock under them as the radiator water in an automobile engine keeps the inside of the cylinders cool.

After ages the heat accumulates sufficiently beneath the continents to liquefy the basalt on which they rest. Once more the continents will be floating freely in the basalt. Now basalt expands when it liquefies, so the Earth will actually increase in diameter, perhaps a few miles. Also, the continental flakes will crack and great spoutings of liquid basalt will stream up. That perhaps is how the great area of basalt in the Deccan in India and in other parts of the Earth originated. The decrease in density of the basalt will cause the continents to sink a little so that the general land levels will be very low, and much land will sink to form shallow seas. With the low-lying land, climates will be hot and sultry. Vegetation will flourish powerfully, and eras will leave great deposits of plant debris to form the coal-measures. Thus the origin of coal is suggested. When the basalt is liquid, tides will be raised in it by the Moon. The tidal action will cause the continents to drift westward, and gradually the hot basalt will be left with a cold solid film over it and the ocean above (fig. 22).

The heat in the liquid basalt will leak through the thin solid layer into the ocean and be transferred away comparatively quickly.

The accumulation of heat below the continent takes about 40,000,000 years; the cooling down about 5,000,000.

Through the whole of the process the ocean bed has been kept cool and solid by the water above, and hence rigid. When the liquid basalt cools and solidifies again there is a contraction in its volume and hence in the volume and the surface of the Earth. The Earth's surface contracts, but the area of the ocean beds remains constant because of their rigidity. So the continents are enormously squeezed. They crumple up and wrinkle, especially at the edges. Hence the Andes, the Alps, the Himalayas.

We are living in an epoch only a few million years after a period of rapid cooling and hence mountain

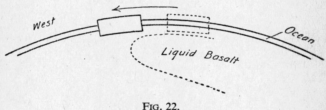

West

Ocean

Liquid Basalt

FIG. 22.

building. When mountains were still higher, glacial ages existed; we have only recently left such behind.

This brilliant theory of Professor Joly's suggests how the continental material should have been kneaded up over and over again into great mountains, how these were levelled out and converted by rain, frost and wind into stretches of strata, only to be crinkled up into mountains once more.

The life of high mountains will generally be short, owing to the severity of the denuding forces their eminence entails. They will be comparatively swiftly worn down and the eras of low-lying land and extensive shallow seas will be much longer than those of mountains. Thus the eternal mountains are seen to be among the more transient of terrestrial features.

XIII

THE ULTIMATE MATERIALS

HAVING arrived at the Earth, the nature of the materials of which the Universe and it are made must be considered. Stone, wood, air, fire, plants, light, animals, water, etc., are all made out of something. They can be resolved into three kinds of entity; the electron, the proton and radiation.

An anthracite coal fire consists of anthracite, air, heat and light. The anthracite is nearly pure carbon which in its turn is a bouquet of twelve protons and twelve electrons. Air consists mainly of oxygen and nitrogen. Oxygen contains sixteen protons and sixteen electrons, while the numbers for nitrogen are fourteen. Then there are the most characteristic properties of the fire, the heat and light from it. These are radiations. All material objects can be analysed into these three entities.

What are these three entities? Electrons are unit parts of negative electricity, protons are unit parts of positive electricity, while radiation is something like light, a process which enables energy arising in one place to become evident in another, without loss by the way. For instance, the fire sends forth heat which warms people sitting in front of it, yet the heat loses virtually nothing in the space between the fire and the people. Some process exists for transferring heat across empty space.

Consider a radio loud-speaker as a material object. It consists mainly of metal, a noise, and radiation.

The metal and other solid parts consist of bouquets

of protons and electrons. The noise is due to the vibrating of part of the metal against the air. Taking up the percussions the air transmits them from bumping atom to bumping atom until the ear is struck and the sensation of sound felt. Metal, the air, parts of the ear; all these consist of proton and electron bouquets. Then there are the radiations which set the whole thing in action. These came through space from some broadcasting station, or, in the case of atmospherics, from a lightning flash. The influences activating the receiving set and hence the loud-speaker, and the warming of the feet at the fire, are called radiation. The huge energy sent from the Sun to the Earth crosses without loss the space between. This gigantic transmission of energy which made the coal measures, oil, the cycle of evaporation from the sea and deposition of water to form rivers and sources of water-power, is an overwhelming example of radiation.

Experiments show that radiation seems to be a wave-motion. A motion of this kind can cause effects at a distance without leaving a permanent impression by the way. For instance, suppose you have a bowl of paraffin oil which has been kept in a very dusty place. Dust will have settled on the sides of the bowl right down to the surface of the liquid. If a pellet is dropped into the middle of the bowl ripples will start out to the sides of the bowl, and will cause a little wash up and down there. After the liquid has become still again, there will be a narrow white clean rim above the edge of the surface all round the bowl. The particles of dust have been removed and energy was required to do that. The energy was transmitted from the splash to the rim by the ripple-waves. Since the surface was the same after having settled as it was in the beginning, the wave-motion has left no trace of itself by the way.

Wave-motions have certain distinct properties. For instance, suppose two pellets of the same size were dropped at the same time into the bowl mentioned above. A particle of dust on the rim near the surface might find itself urged upwards by the ripple from one pellet and urged downwards by the ripple reaching it at the same time from the other pellet. It would move only a slight distance, a resultant of the contrary urges. On the other hand, if it were urged upwards by both ripples it would rise higher upwards than if by one only, the high-tide level marked by the removal of the dust would be seen to be higher when the disturbance on the paraffin had subsided.

Wave-motions have the property of interfering with each other, sometimes cancelling each other's effect at any point, and sometimes reinforcing. Any activity suspected of having a wavy nature can be diagnosed by the possibility of this interference of waves. For instance, light was suspected of having a wavy nature, but for a long time the interference of light-waves was not convincingly demonstrated. The difficulty turned out to be due to the very small length of the waves, which proved to be only about one fifty-thousandth of an inch long. Besides interference effects, wave-motions should exhibit some power of turning round corners. Sea-waves show the effect well enough, for the water in a sheltered bay is always disturbed a little in rough weather, owing to the large wave-motions outside spreading round the headlands into the bay. Sound-waves also get round corners, for a motor horn is heard easily (or ought to be) at a blind cross-road before the horn is visible.

A pretty experiment to show the bending and interfering effects of light-waves has been made with a small coin held in front of a point of light. If the source, coin and screen are arranged at appropriate distances, the shadow of the coin on the screen is seen to contain a spot of light as its centre A. The waves of light from the source have bent round the spot and reinforced each other at A to form a bright spot. Around the spot a dark ring is found. This is due to the waves meeting there, cancelling each other, instead of reinforcing. Next to the dark ring is a light, but vaguer ring. Indeed, a succession of rings are visible, fading out gradually as their diameter increases. The number of the rings, the size of the coin, the distances between the screen, coin and source, enable the length of the waves to be calculated. From such data the wave-length of visible light is found to be about one fifty-thousandth of an inch.

Similar effects are obtained with X-rays, but with these the coin must be replaced by a crystal. The

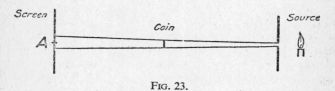

FIG. 23.

X-rays have such very short wave-lengths that the coin must be replaced by minute objects such as the atoms in a crystal. Crystals contain atoms arranged regularly in rows, so one atom can easily be chosen to exert an effect, whereas it would not if all the atoms were jumbled up as in a non-crystalline substance (fig. 24, Plates XII and XIII).

The difference between an atom and a coin suggests how much shorter are the wave-lengths of X-rays than those of light. They are about one ten-millionth of an inch in length. It should be remembered, though, that the comparison between the atom and the coin much exaggerates the difference, because the distance between the screen and source would be very much smaller in the X-ray than in the light experiment.

Interference effects can also be obtained from radio waves. If a broadcasting station is sending waves some of these may go straight from A to B, others may rise at an angle and be reflected at the Heaviside layer, that layer in the upper atmosphere wb ich is able to reflect radio-waves, and arrive at B by another route. The rays following these different paths may well arrive

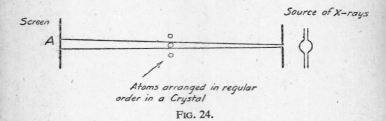

Atoms arranged in regular order in a Crystal

FIG. 24.

at B out of step, one causing a wave-rise as the other causes a wave-fall. In that case they will cancel each other, and a very faint or no signal will be heard from the receiver. If they arrive in step an extra loud signal will be heard. These radio fading effects are well known, and show the wave nature of wireless radiation.

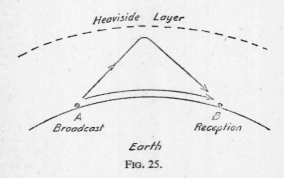

FIG. 25.

Radiation has other characteristics besides those of waves. When its wave-length is very short, it tends more and more to have some of the properties of bullets. For instance, suppose a beam of X-rays is

beer appears as an example to unaided human senses.

At an early stage of the experimental study of electricity, Faraday found evidence that electricity had a property of existing in packets of a certain quantity. He made the first quantitative study of the process upon which electro-plating depends. He inquired exactly how much electricity was used when a certain quantity of silver was deposited on the object being silver-plated. He found that one gramme of silver required always the same quantity of electricity E to deposit it. One gramme of silver contains a certain number of silver atoms, say N, so it would be reasonable to assert that each atom of silver required an $\frac{E}{N}$ quantity of electricity to deposit it. Represent $\frac{E}{N}$ by e. We may say one atom of silver is deposited by a quantity of electricity represented by e.

Faraday found in the same way that aluminium atoms required a quantity of electricity $3e$ to cause them to be decomposed from their compounds. Atoms of substances in the process of electroplating always seemed to require a quantity of electricity e, $2e$, $3e$ . . . or some small multiple, to cause them to be deposited.

Though the fact that atoms always require definite quantities of electricity is suggestive, it does not prove electricity is granular in nature. Humans always drink half-pints, pints, quarts, etc., of beer, but the fact that beer is always handled by human atoms in pint-quantities does not prove a pint of beer is the ultimate unit of beer, that beer exists only in half-pints and multiples of half-pints. Faraday and other physicists were very well aware of this argument and regarded the quantity of electricity e required to deposit one atom of silver rather as a pint of electricity, i.e., a convenient natural unit which did not imply e was not further sub-divisible into spoonfuls and drops of electricity, as it were.

They assumed nature had doled out to atoms sups of electricity of constant quantity, but assumed that if the sups were not given to the atoms but placed into a tank they would all run together into a uniform fluid, and not pile up as if they resembled solid grains of corn.

Faraday himself was the chief developer of the ideas of electricity as a continuous infinitely divisible entity. His powerful imagination visualised the ideas subsequently reduced to mathematical statement by Clerk Maxwell. Faraday was interested in the subtle behaviour of electric forces in space and said that "the seat of the disturbance is in the dielectric", i.e., outside the wire carrying the current. He directed the attention of scientists away from the atoms and their individual quantities of electricity towards the behaviour of electric forces in space, inspiring Maxwell to the theoretical discovery of radio-waves.

For this reason, no one's attention was powerfully directed to the quantity of electricity e which silver atoms require when they are deposited in electroplating. No one said: "Let us assume, just for fun, that electricity cannot exist in quantities less e. What would the consequences be?" If some commanding genius had done, perhaps the history of physics would have been changed greatly, perhaps not.

Fifty years after Faraday's experiments, in 1891, Johnstone Stoney explained that Faraday's experiments implied electricity existed in unit charges of quantity e, and suggested the name *electron* for this unit.

The next series of evidences for unit quantities of electricity came from the study of the passage of electricity through gases; the first from the passage of electricity through liquids in Faraday's electrolysis experiments, the second from corresponding phenomena in gases.

If the pressure of the air in a glass tube with terminals A and B is reduced, it is found that electricity flows much more easily through the tube. At atmospheric pressures the electricity will not pass through unless the current voltage is very high, and then it jumps from A to B in the form of strong sparks. As the pressure is reduced the passage of electricity becomes steadier and gentler. At pressures of one ten-thousandth of an atmosphere luminous rays are seen to spread out from the negative terminal A towards B. The rays reaching the glass of the tube cause it to fluoresce with a green light, and they are bent by a magnet. This was a very important point because it showed the cathode rays (i.e., the rays from the negative terminal) carried electric charges. They were different from light and radio rays not bent by magnets and carrying no electric charges.

FIG. 29.

The problem was to devise experiments which would give quantitative data of these rays. How was the material of a shadowy luminance in the exhausted tube to be weighed and measured? Sir J. J. Thomson solved this problem in 1897. He showed the rays behaved as if they were particles of a certain weight carrying a certain quantity of electricity. His quantitative results revealed very surprising data.

On the evidence of Faraday's experiments one atom of silver was found to be associated with a quantity of electricity e. In all of the electrolysis experiments the weight of element associated with e was of the order of the weight of an atom. In Sir J. J. Thomson's experiment e was found to be associated with a quantity of matter whose mass was about two thousand times lighter than the weight of the lightest atom, hydrogen.

Of course, it was possible to argue that the mass was that of a hydrogen atom, with a charge about 2,000 *e*. Only the ratio of charge to mass was positively known from Sir J. J. Thomson's first experiments.

The rays must consist either of very light particles with charge *e* or of ordinary atoms with charge about 2,000 *e*. It was found that the rays had similar properties from whatever gas they were obtained. Cathode rays from oxygen, nitrogen, hydrogen or any other gas all had this remarkable property.

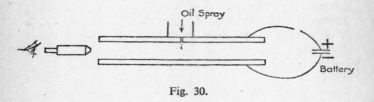

Fig. 30.

There was a strong presumption that the particles had a charge *e* but were actually only one two-thousandth the weight of hydrogen atoms. They were obtainable from all gases, therefore they were probably tiny bits off the atoms of these gases. In fact, their weight was really the weight of the electric charge *e* itself, the weight of the unit of electricity.

Other experiments confirmed the presumption that the particles in the cathode rays were much lighter than ordinary atoms and had the charge *e*. A refined development of these experiments was devised by Millikan, and gave an accurate measure of *e* (fig. 30).

He forced a fine spray of oil into a chamber consisting of two horizontal metal plates. The exceedingly small drops could be watched by the microscope. The drops were so small that they sank through the air very slowly. Millikan found that if electrons were freed in the chamber they attached themselves to the oil-drops, giving them an electric charge.

The speed at which any drop falls through the air depends on its size and weight. Consequently, if its material is known and the speed is observed in the microscope, the weight of the drop can be calculated. So when these falling drops picked up an electric charge, Millikan already knew the weight of the drop. Suppose the lower plate of the chamber were attached to the negative terminal of an electric battery. The negative charge on the plate would repel upwards any of the oil-drops negatively charged by an electron. From a knowledge of the weight of the oil-drop and the size of the charge on the lower plate required to prevent the drop falling farther, Millikan calculated the amount of electricity in the charge e.

Millikan observed another very important effect in this experiment. He noticed that sometimes the charge was equal to $2e$, $3e$, $4e$, etc., because the drop rose twice, etc., times as quickly as usual when the bottom plate was charged. He never found the drops rising $2\frac{1}{2}$ times as fast, or a third as fast; only multiple integral times as fast. This was a strong proof that electric charges vary by fixed amounts only; electricity is not a continuous fluid but a congregation of tiny particles. The particles are so small that only in very special experiments is it necessary to regard electricity as other than a continuous entity.

When the quantity e is known the weight of atoms can be calculated. For instance, Sir J. J. Thomson's method of finding the ratio between e and its own mass or the mass of any larger atomic particle to which it is attached, may be employed.

Faraday's electrolytic results can be used with more accuracy. His work showed that an ounce of silver or hydrogen or any other element required a certain quantity of electricity to liberate it. If this quantity of electricity was divided by e, the number of electrons in it could be calculated. Knowing that each electron was attached to one atom, or two or so electrons to one atom, the number of atoms in an ounce of silver or hydrogen was known at once. This calculation shows that an ounce of hydrogen contains about seventeen billion billion (seventeen million million million million) atoms.

The study of cathode rays has contributed profoundly to the modern knowledge of nature. They have also been turned to much utility. Since the cathode rays are a stream of particles of negative electricity they can be displaced by magnets or electric forces. The rays can behave like a moving finger of light and reveal the forces acting on them. Since they are made of particles of extremely small weight the rays can be bent extremely quickly; their inertia is insignificant.

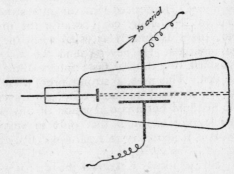

FIG. 31.   Cathode ray oscillograph.

This exceeding sensitiveness to changes in electrical forces enables the cathode rays to register the effect of lightning flashes on radio apparatus.

A cathode ray tube is designed with a flat end so that the rays strike the centre. If the end is covered with some substance which fluoresces when struck by the rays, a green spot of light may be seen in the centre of the end. If a plate is fixed inside the tube parallel to the rays, and connected to an aerial, "atmo-

spherics" will charge the plate electrically and cause
the rays to bend and the green spot to jump.   By
fixing another plate at right angles to the first and
connecting it to an aerial arranged at right angles to
the first aerial, the cathode rays become both a direc-
tion-finder and a measurer of the strength of "atmospherics".

The cathode rays jump from the centre and back
again in the ten-thousandth of a second or less during

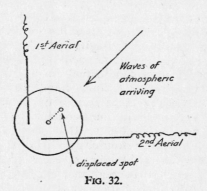

FIG. 32.

which the lightning flash causing the atmospheric
lasted. The effect of fluorescence in the substance
lasts longer than the time taken to stimulate it, so the
eye can watch the fluorescence dying away during a
large fraction of a second. An effect lasting a fifth
of a second is caused by one lasting only one ten-
thousandth of a second.

XV

THE PROTON

THE discovery of the electron in 1897 caused the theory
of electricity to become more complex. The electron

was a negatively charged particle of electricity evidently obtainable from any specimen of ordinary matter. It was much smaller than atoms of substances, and presented itself as very distinct from atoms of elements such as oxygen, silver, etc. Here was the negative particle of electricity, entirely different from any other known particle.

Since bodies are not ordinarily charged with electricity, and behave as if neutral, they must contain positive electricity. The crumbs of bread we eat must contain positive electricity as well as electrons, or they would fly apart. If they consisted entirely of electrons, they would contain entirely negative electric charges, and like charges always repel each other. Indeed, two crumbs if they were made entirely of electrons would repel each other with a force comparable with the weight of the earth. Since crumbs do not repel each other with such force they must contain about as much positive as negative electricity. That positive electricity must resemble negative electricity was naturally assumed. No positively charged particles resembling electrons could be found. How odd that negative electricity should be easily identifiable, while positive electricity was not. Even ten years after the discovery of the electron, the nature of its positive counterpart was obscure. By 1913 the nature of the positive unit became fairly clear, but not by direct experiment. The evidence of its nature has always been indirect, and conclusions on indirect evidence are always slower than on direct, for they are obtained by eliminating the alternatives instead of seizing the essential, proceeding from the outside inwards instead of directly to the inside.

The nature of positive electricity was revealed through Rutherford's conception of the atom. This supreme image suggested innumerable experiments which together showed what positive electricity must be. Rutherford conceived the atom to consist of a tiny heavy nucleus with electrons circulating round it.

The mass of the atom necessarily resided in the nucleus because the very light electrons circulating round it could not contribute much to the total mass. Since the electrons outside were electrically negative, the nucleus must contain an excess of positive electricity to preserve the electrical neutrality of the atom as a whole. Knowledge of the nucleus must lead to knowledge of the nature of positive electricity.

Rutherford's model of the atom at once suggested why negative electricity was so easily obtained from almost any substance. In the cathode-ray and vacuum-tube experiments the outer electrons were being detached

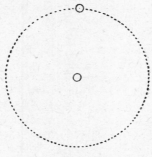

FIG. 33.

from the atom. Being at a comparatively great distance from the nucleus they were lightly held to the atom and easily detached. The positive electricity was concentrated in the centre, and very tightly held. Evidently in all ordinary chemical reactions between atoms their outsides consisting of electrons would be the main determinants of action. The positive electricity being concentrated in the centre would not give any direct evidence of its existence in ordinary experiments with atoms.

An entirely different kind of experiment was required to investigate the nature of the positively charged

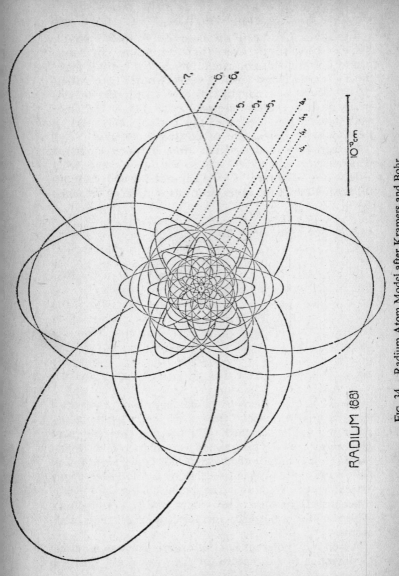

RADIUM (88)

7. 6₂ 6₁ 5₃ 5₂ 5₁ 4₄ 4₃ 4₂ 4₁

10⁻⁸cm

Fig. 34. Radium Atom Model after Kramers and Bohr.

nucleus. This was found first by exploiting the properties of radio-active substances.

Recently Dr. P. A. M. Dirac has published some very interesting calculations bearing on the nature of the proton. His work suggests the proton is really an absence of an electron. He conceives the whole of space to be filled with electrons except in certain places or "holes". The hole marking the absence of an electron manifests itself as a proton. Dr. Dirac advances an ingenious illustration of his idea. An atom consists of a nucleus with electrons circulating round it in rings. Suppose an electron were absent from one of the inner rings, the atom would have a hole in it, as it were, a hole marking the place of an absent electron. The behaviour of an atom with such a "hole" is known and the lacuna causes it to behave somewhat as if it were a proton. Thus absence of electrons tends to be equivalent to presence of protons. Are all protons merely electron-absences? The great difficulty in the idea is that protons are nearly two thousand times heavier than electrons. Why should the absence of an electron be manifested by the existence of a mass two thousand times greater? This problem is unsolved but possibly not insoluble. If soluble, electricity will have been reduced to one kind of entity and the stuff of the universe to two: electrons and radiation.

In fig. 34 we give a model of the radium atom based on Bohr's ideas by Kramers. The intricate interlacing of lines represents possible orbits of electrons revolving round the nucleus. Though this model is now superseded it describes some at least of the features of the radium atom. The complication of the figure indicates the complexity of the mathematics necessary to describe the structure and behaviour of a heavy atom such as that of radium.

XVI

RADIO-ACTIVITY

AN atom consists of a nucleus with electrons revolving round it. What would happen if the nucleus exploded? Some or all of the particles, if any, in the nucelus would fly out, probably with very great force. The substances of chemistry such as carbon, iron, oxygen, etc., have never themselves been changed by heat, or pressure or exposure to intense electric sparks. Only compounds of iron, oxygen, etc., can be damaged by these means. The prospect of causing the atom to explode and thus find what it was made of did not seem very hopeful. Very luckily, nature herself provides examples of exploding atoms, and the messages the ejected parts bring from the nucleus have revealed a new aspect of reality, as the code of the Rosetta Stone revealed the meaning of the Egyptian hieroglyphics.

Radio-active substances exist in the Earth in very small and widely diffused quantities. Traces of their existence were first discovered by Becquerel in Paris in 1896. The stimulation of the discovery of X-rays in 1895 had caused scientists to hunt everywhere for unusual rays of any kind, and Becquerel found that salts of the metal uranium gave rays capable of affecting photographic plates wrapped in black paper.

A year or two before this time, a Polish refugee called Marie Sklodovska was given a job as a bottle-washer in the physics department at the Sorbonne. Her professor, Lippmann, who invented colour-photography, promoted her to preparing apparatus and set her to work with his assistant Curie. In 1895 Curie married Sklodovska.

Mme Curie discovered uranium salts contained a fraction which emitted rays much more powerfully than uranium itself. She isolated the fraction and named it radium. For these researches she received the Nobel Prize in 1911 and shared a Nobel Prize with her husband and Becquerel in 1903. Thus she is the only woman to receive a Nobel Prize, and the only person to receive more than one.

If an atom consisting of electrons and protons explodes, single and groups of electrons and protons will probably be flung out of it. There will probably also be something corresponding to the flash of light from dynamite. Just as the extreme agitation of particles in exploding dynamite causes light, so will the agitation of the electrons and protons in the exploding atom cause a radiation similar to light.

In general, these are the actual events observed when atoms explode. When a uranium atom explodes it shoots forth a group consisting of four protons and two electrons, and also two free electrons. The quakes caused by their departure travel forth from the atom as radiations resembling X-rays of great penetrating power. After a time the remainder of the uranium atom flings forth another electron. After another wait, still another. The third remainder lives for a time and then shoots out another group of four protons and two electrons together with two free electrons. The fourth remainder readjusts itself after the losses in either of two ways. Ninety-two times out of a hundred it readjusts itself into Ionium, eight times into Uranium γ. Presently the Ionium shoots out a group of four protons and two electrons, together with two free electrons, and the remainder is the substance Radium. Alternatively the U_γ loses an electron, and then the group of four protons and two electrons and two free electrons to form the substance Actinium. And so the process continues. Some of the substances have the chance of existing thousands of millions of

years before exploding, others less than one thousandth
of a second.

Single radio-active atoms are observed not to explode
according to any determined time-scheme, one can
say only the chances are that an atom of radium will
last for about 1,700 years. The atoms do not behave
as if they contained a time-fuse which caused them to

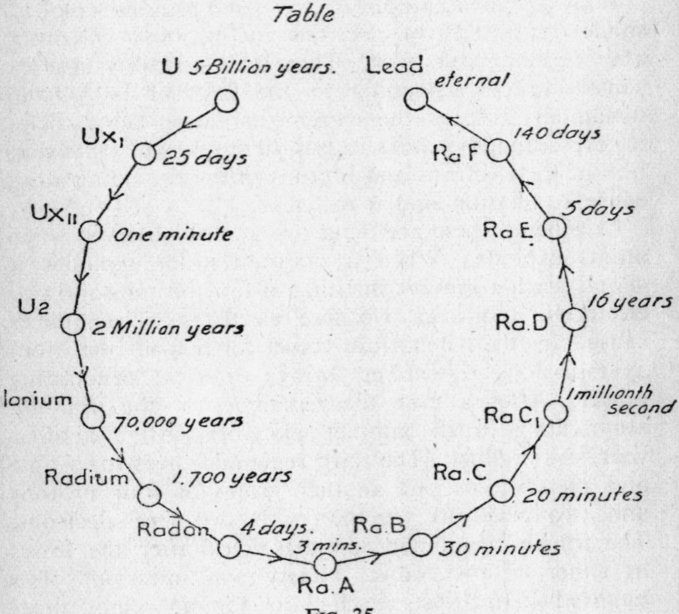

Table

Fig. 35.

explode after a certain time. The occasion of an atomic
explosion appears to be entirely fortuitous. An atom
of radium might exist almost for ever, but if it did,
another would have to explode almost immediately
after both were born from the uranium transformations
to keep the average life of radium atoms down to about
1,700 years.

The series of the uranium explosions and the average lives of the products are given in fig. 35.

The radio-active changes are very varied, and the rate at which a group of protons or electrons is flung out of an exploding atom depends on the substance. Not all of these groups are flung out at the same rate from different substances. Neither are the free electrons shot out with the same speed from all radio-active substances, nor radiation of the same wave-length. The variety of the speeds and wave-lengths of the messengers from exploding nuclei show how complicated the forces inside must be, and a study of them provides data from which the nuclear structure can be imagined. With some advance knowledge of what radio-activity is like, the significance of the great experiments with radio-active substances becomes clearer.

Rutherford was the leader in the investigation of the nature of the things flung forth from exploding atoms.

He placed a very thin glass tube near some radium. The group of four protons and two electrons flung forth had just enough momentum to go through one side of the glass tube but not on and out through the other side. Presently the tube filled with these groups of particles in quantity sufficient to be identified spectroscopically, and their nature as nuclei of atoms of the gas helium became evident. In combination with another, this beautiful experiment may also be used for determining the number of atoms in an ounce of substance (fig. 36).

These groups of particles flung out of exploding atoms shoot forth with such violence that each one, in spite of its excessively small size (there are many billion billion of them to the ounce), is able to make its presence visible. The fact that a million million million millionth part of an ounce of radium possesses enough energy to show its position indicates the prodigious degree of atomic energy. If this small part of radium can cause a visible spark, then an ounce of radium if it exploded all at once could make a flash a million million million million times as big, i.e. it would make a momentary flash comparable with that

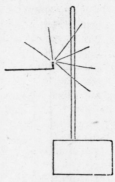

Fig. 36.

of a vast volcano or a million million candle-power search-light. The effect is well exhibited by Crookes' Spinthariscope (fig. 37).

Radium is placed on a small support at R. Near it is a screen S covered with zinc sulphide. The screen

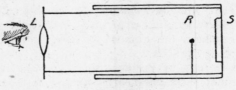

Fig. 37.

is observable through the lens L. As many of the particles shoot forth from the radium they strike the atoms of zinc sulphide on S and cause a tiny green flash. The number of flashes per minute from a known quantity of radium at R enables the number per minute at which the particles are being shot out to be calculated. Consequently, if a known quantity of radium is placed near the closed thin glass tube the number of helium nuclei it brings to the tube per minute and per month is known. At the end of a month or more this quantity can be estimated chemically, so both the number of atoms in, and the weight of, the sample of helium are known. The number of atoms per ounce found by this method agrees remarkably well with the result obtained

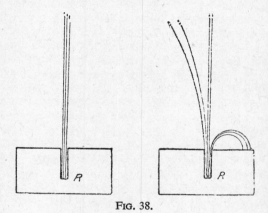

FIG. 38.

from the data of electrolysis and Millikan's value of *e*.

Another revealing experiment on the radio-active rays is made by subjecting them to magnetic and electric forces, as in J. J. Thomson's experiment on the cathode rays.

If a quantity of radium is placed at the bottom of a deep narrow hole in a block of lead, the radiations reaching the air will come forth from the hole as a narrow beam. If this beam is placed in a strong magnetic field particles carrying a positive electric charge will be bent in one direction, those with a negative charge in the opposite, while rays with no charge will remain undeviated. The deviations will be proportional to the charges and speeds of the charged particles. In the experiment the heavy group-particles are found to carry a positive, while the light particles carry a negative charge. There is also an undeviated beam, the radiation of wave character. The group-particles are observed to be four times the weight of hydrogen atoms and the light particles similar in every respect to electrons.

The deviation of the electrons flung out of exploding radium is immensely significant not only of the structure of the radium nucleus, but also for the whole framework of nature. Some of the ejected electrons move at very high speeds almost equal to the velocity of light. According to Einstein's theory of relativity objects in movement increase their weight, but the increase is too small to become evident except at speeds approaching that of light. These high-speed electrons are moving fast enough to exhibit this increase in weight, and indeed the increase has been observed. Their paths are not bent as much as they would be if their weight remained equal to that at ordinary speeds. Radioactivity provides one of the best proofs of the theory of relativity besides the evidence for the structure of the atom.

XVII

SPEED OF a-PARTICLES

THE speed of the large group-particles which prove to be nuclei of helium is equally interesting and has led to great scientific discoveries. The group-particles may move at speeds up to about one-tenth the velocity of light, i.e., from 10,000 to 15,000 miles per second. At first this looks much less useful than the speed of electrons which may move with ·998 of the velocity of light or about 186,000 miles a second. But the helium nuclei consist of four protons and two electrons, so they are about 7,400 times as heavy as a electron. The energy of a moving body is proportional to the weight multiplied by the square of the speed, and helium nuclei are so much heavier than electrons even when the latter's actual weight is increased owing to the relativity effect, that helium nuclei at 10,000 miles a second contain about a dozen times as much energy as the fastest known electrons. Consequently, a high-speed helium nucleus can deliver a much severer blow and penetrate much more incisively than the fastest known electron, and is more potent for many purposes as an instrument of scientific investigation.

The fundamental data from which the modern conception of the atom was deduced were obtained from experiments with the heavy helium nuclei discharged by radium products. An early experiment with cathode rays also provided one of the chief clues.

Lenard had noticed that the electrons in cathode rays had the power of passing through thin aluminium windows fixed in the side of glass vacuum tubes. Since the atoms of aluminium were known to be packed together tightly, since solid and liquid aluminium is about equally bulky and, like all substances in those states, very resistant to compression, and there must be a layer of them millions thick in even very thin foil, the electrons must have passed right through many of the atoms. This implied the atoms must be very spacious, a most revolutionary idea. Until this experiment atoms had been conceived as impenetrable balls, as they seem to be from their behaviour under compression. By studying the scattering of the electrons by the atoms in the foil, Lenard made certain deductions about the structure of aluminium atoms. He was able to say that a certain area of the aluminium atom was impenetrable to flying electrons. His experiments were very difficult because of the lightness of the electrons and

their sensitiveness to deflections. Suppose the dotted
lines represent the boundaries of the aluminium foil
and the large circles the boundaries of the aluminium
atoms in the foil (fig. 39). The dots are the nuclei of
the atoms. The arrows 1, 2, 3, 4, represent the paths of
electrons in the cathode rays falling on to the foil from

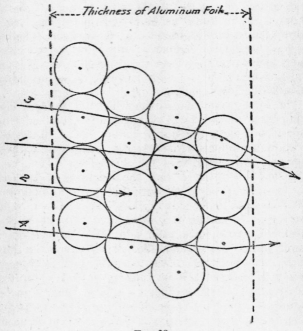

FIG. 39.

the left. No. 1 goes right through the foil, hitting nothing.
No. 2 runs into a nucleus and stops. No. 3 goes near
two nuclei and is swung round and leaves the foil at
an angle. No. 4 is scattered in a similar way. From a
study of the number which get right through like No.
1, the number entirely stopped, including those like

No. 2 and the angles at which those such as Nos. 3 and 4 emerge, the extent of the spaciousness of the atom may be roughly deduced, and the size and charge on the nuclei. The results are not easy to interpret because of the deflectability of the electrons. Less flexible atomic scouts were required. These were found in the heavy helium nuclei ejected from radio-active atoms, and exploited by Rutherford.

A narrow beam of helium nuclei was directed on to aluminium foil. A screen covered with zinc sulphide was placed beyond the foil (fig. 40). The helium nuclei in many cases went straight through and made scintillations as with Nos. 2 and 3. Others were deflected as 1, 4. The average amount of deflection was shown

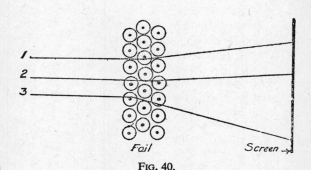

Fig. 40.

from its quantity to be the sum of many small deflections of the nuclei as they passed near aluminium atoms. There were also a few very large deflections of abnormal size (fig. 41).

The particle turned backwards. It was found that with thicker foil there were more cases of extreme deviation. This was a very remarkable discovery. The particles were not merely rebounding from the surface, but from the interior also. Occasionally they approached a nucleus in the interior of the foil,

rebounded, and shot back out of the foil! (fig. 42).
The idea of a particle going right through a metal
foil without hitting anything is sufficiently surprising,
but the idea of its penetrating to the middle and coming

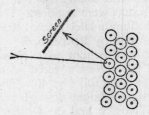

FIG. 41.

back again on the rebound from a nucleus without
otherwise hitting anything is astonishing.

Rutherford deduced that the nucelus must be very
massive to be able to act as a buffer. From the frequency of the abnormally large deflections the size of
the nucleus could be estimated. It proved to be about
two ten-million-millionths of an inch in diameter, and

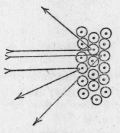

FIG. 42.

smaller than an electron thousands of times lighter.
Presumably the protons and electrons in a nucleus
are condensed together somehow to less than their
independent size. From the size of the angles through

which the particles were scattered the electric charge on the nucleus was deduced. It was positive and equal to about one unit for hydrogen, two units for helium, three units for lithium, four for beryllium, five for boron, six for carbon, seven for nitrogen, and in general, half the atomic weight for the light elements. For the heavy elements the values were less than half the atomic weight and not very precise. These results were very suggestive, since they revealed a step-by-step increase in the electric charges on the nuclei of the known atoms in the order of their increase in atomic weight. They confirmed the idea that the elements are different sized groups of simpler things. If the increases in charge had not been regular and integral, the nuclei could not have been so confidently suspected of being groups of fundamental entities of standard size, such as protons and electrons.

These results were confirmed and extended by a research of an entirely different kind made by H. G. J. Moseley. This young scientist made his famous discovery at the age of twenty-six, and was killed in Gallipoli two years later in 1915, after orders had already been made to recall him from the trenches and put him to scientific research. No greater man was ever so needlessly sacrificed.

Moseley bombarded specimens of various elements with cathode rays. When the electrons in atoms of the specimens are struck by the flying electrons in the cathode rays, they are thrown into a state of vibration. The electrons in the outer rings of the atoms are caused to emit X-rays of the usual type. These X-rays become more penetrating the swifter the cathode rays used in their production.

Another set of X-rays is also produced. The wavelength of these is found to be independent of the speed of the cathode rays used to excite them, and apparently to depend on the fixed time of vibration of something stable within the atom and not easily moved, as the outer electrons. Moseley measured the wave-length of these X-rays and showed that they increased by perfectly even amounts as the atomic weight of the element increased. He argued that the evenness of the increase must be due to something which increased evenly in the nucleus. This would probably be the electric charge on the nucleus. When he found there was a double gap between the wave-lengths given by elements thought not to have any element of inter-mediate properties between them, he prophesied that a new element might be discovered. He showed that the charge on the nucleus of the hydrogen atom was unity, and the charge on that of uranium was the largest and equal to 92 units. He concluded there were exactly 92 elements and pointed out that several, such as those with 61 and 72 units of electricity on their nuclei, had yet to be found. A search was made for these, and they have been found. Now only two elements remain undiscovered, those with nuclear charges of 85 and 87 units respectively.

Naturally the elements are numbered if they are made out of sets of protons and electrons. Integral parts are not indefinitely subdivisible.

In Rutherford's experiments on the behaviour of particles ejected from radio-active substances as they pass through matter, there was nothing to see except occasional green sparks under a microscope. From the distribution of the green sparks on the screen and the rate at which they appeared, he collected the data from which the modern conception of the atom was imagined. The slender means by which such great results were obtained will excite more and more admir-ation in the future, and show the vast imaginative power of the discoverer, as the accumulation of knowledge will make obvious that which in 1911 was a divination from comparatively few facts.

Rutherford deduced the general structure of the atom chiefly from the behaviour of certain green sparks or scintillations. He showed the nucleus must be about two ten-million-millionths of an inch in diameter.

The most powerful microscope will not reveal bodies less than about one one-hundred-thousandth of an inch in diameter. The ultra-microscope will show the position and give some idea of the features of bodies about ten times smaller. Thus the nucleus of an atom is about ten million times too small to be detected by a microscope. It is apparently beyond the range of observation.

Yet the movements of bodies of the same order of size can be watched, as in the experiment of Millikan to determine the size of the electric charge on the electron. The method was invented by C. T. R. Wilson in 1898. In his studies of the formation of clouds he noticed that cloud began to form at points when the temperature of cool air was lowered, and not every-where at once. Sir J. J. Thomson suggested some of these points might be electrons, in which case the appearance of cloud would indicate the position of a body of size of the order a million-millionth of an inch in diameter. The electrons betrayed their presence because the charge on them attracted water-vapour molecules, as bits of paper are attracted by a rubbed fountain-pen cap. It was quite possible for a particle only a million-millionth of an inch in diameter to collect round it a cluster of water-vapour molecules each a million times bigger than itself, and the whole cluster large enough to be seen under a powerful microscope. Millikan's experiment was a develop-ment of this technique.

Wilson showed how the places of electrons and charged particles could be detected from possible cloud condensation on the particles. To show the position of such a particle was an astonishing achievement, but to show the track of one of these particles when moving quickly seemed impossible. The water-vapour particles would necessarily fail to stick to the fast-moving particle, just as a group of soldiers who could perfectly well betray to a person miles away the whereabouts of a stationary bullet by clustering round it, would fail to show the track of the flying bullet by accompanying it on its trajectory through the air at 2,000 feet a second. Even less so, for helium nuclei from radium travel at 10,000 miles a second. How could the track of a particle less than a million-millionth of an inch in diameter and travelling at 10,000 miles a second be revealed ? The problem seemed impossible.

In 1911 C. T. R. Wilson solved it, and his original apparatus and pictures will always be studied with emotion by scientists. Wilson showed how the tracks of these incredibly minute and swiftly moving particles could be revealed, and scientists felt they had been given sight into a new world, the sub-atomic universe.

The normal atom consists of a nucleus with a group of electrons circulating round it like planets round a sun. When it is struck by a flying nucleus some of the outside electrons are struck or brushed off. These fall by the wayside, as it were, and many of them are just brushed off without gaining much speed themselves. A flying nucleus leaves a track of detached electrons by its way. It also leaves a large number of atoms minus the brushed-off electrons. These atoms will have lost one, two or more electrons, so they will have a large positive electric charge. They are thousands of times heavier than electrons because they contain the heavy nuclei. By virtue of their weight they will not in general recoil far from the disturbed track of the flying nucleus. These charged, or ionised, atoms and electrons in the neighbourhood of the track would act as excellent cloud-manufacturers, given the chance.

Wilson conceived the idea of arranging that the radioactive substances ejected their flying particles into air just about to be cooled.

Immediately after the particle flew, the moist air was cooled by expansion and the water-vapour condensed on the ionised atoms and electrons lying along the track. An instantaneous photograph revealed the thin streak of cloud marking the particle's path. A particle less than a million-millionth of an inch in diameter and travelling at more than 10,000 miles a second had been traced, and the trace photographed! Scientists are silent with admiration for the genius of this experiment (Plate XIV).

XVIII

DISINTEGRATION OF THE ATOM

THE green scintillations caused by the impact of particles ejected from radio-active substances against zinc sulphide screens provided the data for the conception of the Rutherford atom. By their means also Rutherford demonstrated the disintegration of the atom.

The helium nuclei flung out of radio-active atoms have a well-defined range in air. They cannot penetrate beyond a certain distance because their energy has been frittered down by the passage through the millions of atoms of oxygen and nitrogen in their way. If the zinc sulphide screen were placed beyond the range no scintillations were seen. At least, scintillations were visible in thousands if the screen were placed just within the extreme range, and none when the screen was just beyond the range. Or almost none. Scintillations were noticed very occasionally to occur when the screen was beyond the normal range. What could these mean? A careful investigation showed these scintillations sometimes occurred when the screen was four times beyond the normal range. From the appearance of the scintilla-

tion its cause was suspected of being small and of very
great speed. If the nitrogen was removed from the
apparatus and pure oxygen substituted for air, the
scintillations disappeared. If the quantity of nitrogen
was varied, the number of abnormal scintillations varied
in proportion to the amount of nitrogen. If certain
other substances containing nitrogen, such as titanium
nitrate, were used instead of air, the number of scintillations was again found to be proportional to the
amount of nitrogen present. By the methods used
for measuring the speed and weight of the particles in
cathode rays, the abnormal scintillations were shown
to be due to particles of about the weight of hydrogen
atoms or nuclei. Rutherford found that if a certain
mixture of hydrogen and carbon dioxide were placed
in the apparatus, exactly similar long-range scintillations could be observed. These must have come
from hydrogen atoms which were struck forward by
the radio-active projectiles. The similarity of the
particles from nitrogen causing long-range scintillations to the struck hydrogen nuclei confirmed their
identification. The long-range scintillations must be
due to hydrogen struck out of the nitrogen atom; the
nitrogen atom must have been disintegrated.

If a flying helium nucleus from a radio-active substance is capable of being traced by Wilson's method
of cloud-formation round its track, the trace of the
impact of such a particle on a nitrogen atom might
perhaps be photographable. Wilson had noticed forks
sometimes appeared in the tracks he had photographed.
The possibility was investigated by P. M. S. Blackett.
He used a form of Wilson's cloud-expansion apparatus
evised by Shimizu to work automatically, and capable
of taking two photographs at right-angles simultaneously. From the two photographs the directions of the
tracks in space could be calculated. Blackett arranged
for the photographs to be taken with cinema cameras.
With these machines he took 23,000 photographs

PLATE XV

(*Blackett.*)

A nitrogen atom was disintegrated at the fork. The fine branch is the track of the hydrogen nucleus knocked out of it and the thick one is that of the damaged nitrogen atom plus the helium nucleus which hit it, i.e. a synthesised oxygen atom.

See page 126.

See page 155.

PLATE XVI

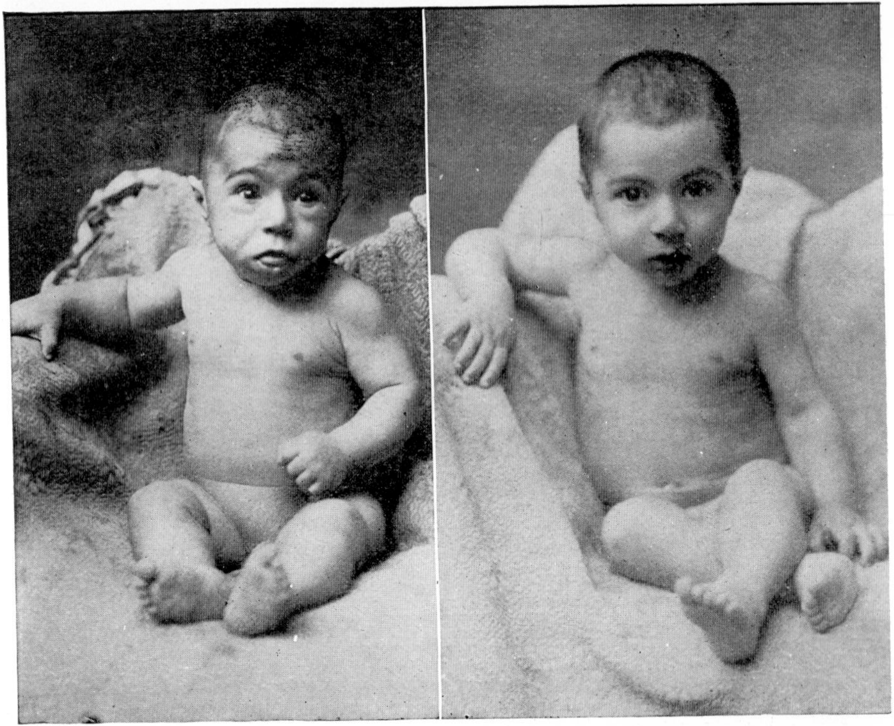

(a)

(b)

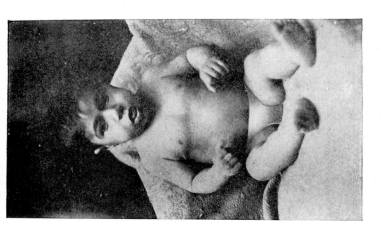

(c)

a) A cretin with an under-active thyroid gland.

(*b*) The same child after treatment with thyroid extract.

The parents thought it was permanently cured and stopped the treatment, and it relapsed with the condition shown in (*c*)

PLATE XVII

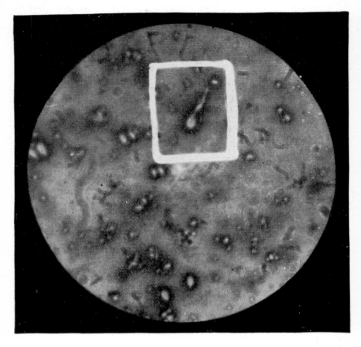

Colloidal Particles to which rubber owes its properties: the particle shape in the latex of a mother rubber tree.

See page 158.

PLATE XVIII

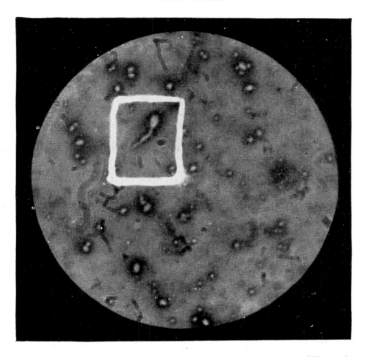

(Hauser.)

Particle in latex of a bud-graft from the same mother-tree—an example of inheritance of a colloidal characteristic of a living organism.

See page 158.

PLATE XIX

(Svedberg.)

Svedberg's Ultra-Centrifuge which produces centrifugal forces up to 125,000 times the force of gravity.

See page 164.

Very many of the fundamental researches in experimental atomic physics have been made by British and Americans. One wonders whether a tradition of ball-games helps researchers instinctively to guess what flying particles will do, and to have a familiarity with them that makes them congenial mental models to play with. Rutherford is a New Zealander, Wilson a Scot, Thomson and Aston and Blackett English, Millikan and Compton are American. Have these investigators unconsciously drawn on their nation-acquired skill in games to help them to interpret atomic phenomena? Has the back-yard baseball and cricket given these nations an almost instinctive understanding of how flying and colliding particles would naturally behave? The German, with his taste for mental recreations, music, philosophy, chess, has tended to see the world from a theoretical perspective. He usually tried to see phenomena in terms of wave-motions that appeal more to the mental speculator, than in terms of particles whose ways were known from childhood.

The history of ball-games is ancient and distinguished. As mentioned in a later chapter they arose probably out of primitive burial-rites, in which two groups of persons, one representing Death and the other Life, wrestled for the mummy of the departed. As the rite evolved the skull only was played with and then a ball substitute. Football and the rest of the ball-games were well on the way. Has the long experience of ball-games starting from primitive burial-rites and culminating in baseball and cricket helped the philosophers who to-day investigate the atomic secrets of nature? Has the passing of skulls in the ancient game of the struggle between Life and Death helped modern men to intuit the behaviour of flying atoms? Perhaps.

E

ANALYSIS OF VICTORIAN ATOMS

THE notorious conventions of the Victorian period were not restricted to social custom. One of the foundations of Victorian respectability lay in the belief in the immutability of what were called atoms. The Victorians believed in the existence of a number of chemical elements, such as iron, hydrogen, oxygen, chlorine, etc. The atoms of these substances were supposed to be truly elementary. Two hundred years earlier, Robert Boyle had insisted that elements were merely substances which had so far defied analysis, but not necessarily further un-analysable. Though this relativitistic view seems natural, the human mind has a tendency to absolutism, and indulged the tendency during the Victorian period. Many scientists acted as if they believed the chemical elements they knew were really elementary. In a way, the oddness of the known chemical elements assisted this belief. The weight of the chlorine atom was 35·46, for example. If it had been 35 or 36, or some other integer, the notion that it consisted of a group of say 35 elementary particles bound together would have been easier to accept. Gold's atomic weight was 197·2, Lead 207·2, Tin 118·70. The oddness of these numbers suggested they represented something fundamental since simple order always suggests underlying law while oddness suggests the rocky uniqueness of fundamental reality. How could an odd number like 35·46 be resolved into a combination of even numbers?

The first insight of the solution came from J. J. Thomson's work on neon, the gas now used in making the red-light advertisement signs. Using his method of analysing rays of charged atoms and electrons by exposing them to combined magnetic and electric fields, he found that among the rays obtained apparently from the gas neon, there were two sorts, one indicating charged particles of weight 20, and the other charged particles of weight 22; his experiment seemed to show two kinds of neon atom existed. This result was confirmed by F. W. Aston, who invented a much more powerful technique for performing the experiment.

Suppose you have a beam of positively charged particles proceeding from A. At E they are subjected to deflection by an electric field, and at M a deflection in the contrary direction by a magnetic field. At P there is a photographic plate.

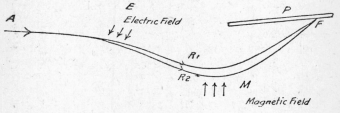

FIG. 43.

The beam will contain charged particles travelling at various speeds. The slower particles of the same weight will be deflected more than the faster-moving particles of the same weight. The beam will split up under the electric field into a band of rays of which R_1, R_2 are samples representing rays due to particles of equal weight but different speeds. If a photographic plate were placed across the dispersed beam at R_1, R_2, only a blur would be obtained owing to the fact that all the particles of weight M would be travelling at different speeds and hence in different rays. If a magnetic field is placed at M, all these rays due to particles of weight M may be deflected back, so that they intersect again at F. At E the beam was resolved, at F it

was put together again. How does that help? you
ask. It happens that only the particles of weight
M collect together again at F. Particles of weight M_1
are found to focus at F_1, and particles of weight M_2 at
F_2, etc.

This most ingenious arrangement causes all the
particles of the same weight M in the beam from A to
collect at the same point F, on the photographic plate
irrespective of their speeds at A. If one particle of mass
M is travelling at 50 miles a second at A, and another
at 70 miles a second, both strike the point F on the
plate.

Aston found that when the rays from neon were

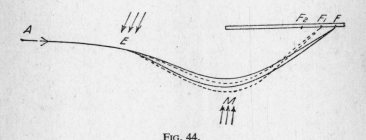

FIG. 44.

analysed there were two distinct foci on the photographic plate corresponding to particles of atomic
weight 20 and 22. With chlorine there were two distinct
foci, one corresponding to 35 and the other to 37.
Besides, the intensity of the line on the photograph
from the 35 focus was about three times as strong as
the line due to the particles of weight 37. This indicated
chlorine must consist of two sorts of atoms, the lighter
being three times as numerous as the heavier. If
that were so, the atomic weight of chlorine would
be $\dfrac{3 \times 35 + 37}{4} = 35 \cdot 5$, which is what it is ! Tin
contains atoms of at least eleven different weights.

Why should the fact that most of the chemical elements have atoms of different weights not have been discovered before? Because chemistry deals only with the chemical properties of atoms, and with matter in bulk. Chemistry never deals with less than about a million million atoms at once. If it could deal with a dozen or a score the results of chemical investigation might show that not all specimens of common salt had the same average density, because one specimen might contain a greater percentage of the 37-weight chlorine atoms than of the other. The mass-spectrograph, as Aston's apparatus is called, will deal with single atoms and only about a thousand atoms are required to bombard the photographic plate in order to leave a mark.

The atoms of the chemical elements have been analysed. Since the method depends on the separate atoms of equal mass focused at one point, the fact that they have been so focused is a proof, indeed the first direct proof, that atoms of any substance are all of the same weight, or set of weights. Previous experiment proved only that the average weight of atoms was such and such. The argument ran: "We know from chemical experiment that a billion atoms weigh so much. Therefore on the average one atom weighs a billionth of this", which does not prove each atom is of that weight.

Aston finds that quantities of atoms of nearly every substance can be analysed into one or more sets, each of whose individual weights is a whole number, taking oxygen as 16. There are some exceptions, among which hydrogen is notable. If oxygen is 16 and nearly all other atoms some whole number, then hydrogen is definitely 1·008. Why? Atoms are groups of protons and electrons. In particular, the nucleus is a group of protons and electrons very closely bound together. For instance, the normal carbon atom can be represented:

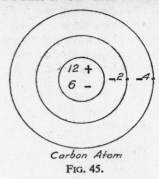

Carbon Atom

FIG. 45.

The nucleus contains twelve protons and six electrons, and there are six electrons revolving round the nucleus in orbits. The nucleus has been proved to be no larger than an electron, so the twelve protons and six electrons must be packed together with extraordinary force. The energy for this must have come from somewhere. According to the theory of relativity, energy is weight, therefore it is suggested some weight has been consumed in packing the nucleus. Hence all other nuclei are naturally slightly less than exact multiples of the weight of the hydrogen nucleus, which is the proton. Aston's researches not only show that nearly all atoms are of integral, or a combination of integral weight, they provide an indirect proof also of the theory of relativity.

If chlorine, mercury, etc., contain atoms of varying weight, they should be analysable by other means. For instance, the lighter atoms should penetrate a porous plug slightly more quickly, and should evaporate more quickly. By using this method, a quantity of chlorine has been slightly separated into two specimens, one of which was denser than the other because it contained a greater percentage of atoms of 37 weight. Mercury has been separated by evaporation into portions one of which was denser than the other. These experiments merely proved a chemical element could have atoms of different weight. They were not sufficiently sensitive to measure the various weights. Their severe limitations show the astonishing quality of the technique invented by J. J. Thomson and F. W. Aston.

XX

ATOMIC STRUCTURE

THE evidence from experiments with cathode rays, radio-active substances, the analysis of chemical atoms of odd atomic weight into two or more sorts each of integral atomic weight, etc., have established that atoms

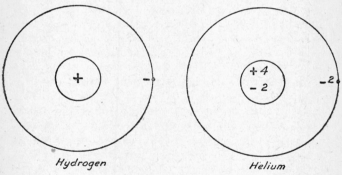

Hydrogen   Helium

FIG. 46.

are groups of protons or nuclei of hydrogen atoms, and electrons.

The hydrogen atom may be represented by a nucleus of one proton with an electron revolving round it. The helium atom has two outer electrons, and a nucleus of four protons and two electrons. If the helium atom loses one of its outer electrons it has a certain similarity to the hydrogen atom, for in that case each atom would consist of two parts only, a positive nucleus encircled by one electron. Niels Bohr explained for the first time that certain rays emitted by excited gas which resembled hydrogen rays, were due to helium atoms which had lost one electron and hence resembled hydrogen atoms.

A sodium atom may be represented as:

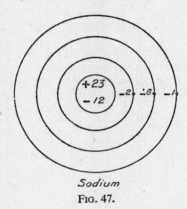

Sodium

FIG. 47.

The nucleus contains 23 protons and 12 electrons. There are two outer electrons fairly near the nucleus, eight others rather farther away, and one lonely electron on the outside. The chlorine atoms are of two sorts, each with a nuclear charge of 17 units, but one nucleus containing 35 protons and 18 electrons, the other containing 37 protons and 20 electrons.

The argon atoms are of at least two kinds, one of mass 40, the other 36. Their electrons are arranged schematically: There are two electrons in the inner shell, eight on the second and eight on the outside of the atom.

Potassium has a nuclear charge of 19. Its atom has four sets of outer electrons.

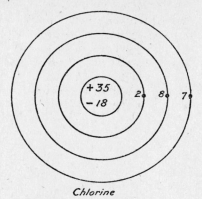

Chlorine

FIG. 48.

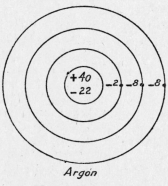

Argon

FIG. 49.

Sodium and potassium resemble each other in having only one electron on the outside of the atom. These metals resemble each other closely, making such similar compounds as potash and soda. Evidently the fact that they have a lone outer electron is closely connected with the similarity in chemical properties. It is to be expected. When atoms combine to make common salt or any other compound, their outsides must be in juxtaposition and presumably chemical affinity is mainly

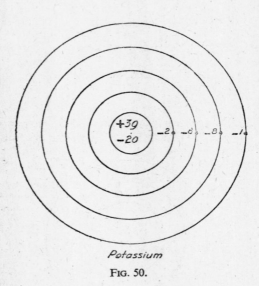

Potassium

FIG. 50.

a function of the surface rather than the interior of atoms.

Chlorine has seven electrons in its outer shell. So has bromine, whose atomic grouping is represented:

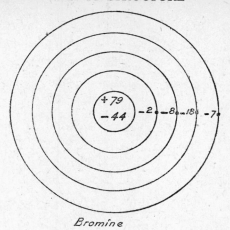

Bromine

FIG. 51.

Chlorine and bromine are chemically similar.

The gas krypton has eight electrons in its outer shell. This gas like argon and helium does not combine with other substances and is entirely inert chemically.

Apparently all atoms which have sets of 2, 8 or 18 electrons on their outsides are chemically inert, all atoms with one outer electron are very active chemically, as sodium and potassium. Atoms with seven outer electrons like chlorine and bromine are also chemically active.

Sodium and chlorine combine together easily to make the stable compound common salt.

The molecules of common salt can be represented as in fig. 53.

The seven outer electrons of the chlorine atom associate with the lone outer electron of sodium to make a group of eight. The sodium atom is always behaving as if it wanted to get rid of its lone electron, while the chlorine atom has a thirst for one electron. Hence sodium and chlorine atoms fall into each other's arms as it were, the deficiencies of each making up for the other. When they are joined to make a molecule of

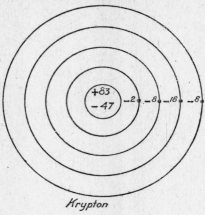

Krypton

FIG. 52.

common salt, the sodium atom can feel as if it had got rid of its outer electron, while the chlorine atom feels

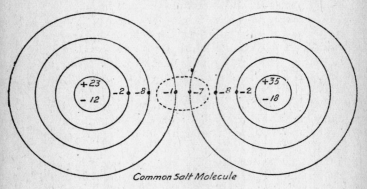

Common Salt Molecule

FIG. 53.

as if it had got eight electrons in its outer group. Thus in combination both atoms behave as if they had eight electrons in their outer shells, sodium by handing over its odd electron to make up chlorine's seven into a set of eight. Sodium then regards its second inner complete set of eight electrons as its boundary. Both atoms feeling they have sets of eight electrons on their outsides behave as if they actually had eight, i.e., as if they were inert, like argon and krypton which do have eight outer electrons. Thus common salt is easy to form and is stable because in its molecules the atoms sodium and chlorine feel as if they were inert. As rest appears to be the object of nature, the atoms are happiest when their condition resembles that of inert atoms. Everyone wonders why a harmless thing like common salt should arise from two such dangerous and active substances as chlorine (the first poison gas used in the war) and sodium (which takes fire when placed on water). The explanation follows simply from the structure of the sodium and chlorine atoms.

The ordinary reactions of chemistry are concerned with the making up of the sets of electrons on the outsides of atoms into sets of 2, 8 or 18. Atoms have their sets made up by sharing their odd electron.

Since many atoms have a large number of outer electrons there is a wide range of possibilities in deficiency. There are 90 known different sorts of atom, and the outer electron systems of all of them can exist in a variety of states, making the chemical variety much greater than 90. Any grouping of atoms able to relieve a deficiency in the number of outer electrons is liable to lead to a chemical compound, and the number of possible groupings of sets from a variety of hundreds of atoms in a condition of outer electron abnormality is very large.

Atomic structure leads to explanations of the physical nature of substances, besides explaining chemical reactions.

Why some substances are coloured and others white, black or transparent, why liquids are liquid, gases gaseous, and solids solid at particular temperatures is becoming clearer.

The great science of chemistry is concerned with the behaviour of substances in bulk. It has been studied by many of the greatest chemists not so much for the technical principles it has revealed for handling matter in bulk, as for the evidence its data provided for discerning the nature of things, the inner structure of matter. To-day chemistry is being valued more and more for its special knowledge of technique, in handling matter, rather than as a source of natural philosophic data. Chemistry is being regarded as allied more to industry than philosophy. It provides the methods for handling raw materials with greater subtlety, producing better food, clothes, dyes, manures, etc. A hundred years ago the scientific philosophers were often chemists, now they are usually atomic physicists. The influence of chemistry is enormous. Consider the effects of the discovery of the process for synthesising ammonia by Haber and his collaborators. This discovery made the Great War possible. If Germany had not been able to make nitrogen compounds for agriculture and munitions she would have collapsed in a few months.

Chemistry describes the interactions of matter in bulk. It is a huge collection of facts and technical details, as a great part of natural history and biology is a description and enumeration of fact. As chemistry describes the nature of matter and its many habits rather than indicates the skeletal ideas embedded in the universe of fact, it is more useful to the task of cataloguing than of outlining the universe. Consequently, chemistry is not as prominent as physics in this book, and less space is given to what are called molar as against atomic properties of matter.

XXI

THE MIND OF CHEMISTRY AND OF PHYSICS

MAN usually starts by getting hold of the wrong end of the stick. In science, especially as an Arab, he accomplished much in the description of substances as found in the familiar temperature range of 0° to a few hundred degrees centigrade. The huge variety of materials possible in that particular temperature range prevented him from discovering more than a few descriptive and very simple quantitative facts about them. Chemistry demanded experimental skill, observation, and a memory capable of retaining many facts. An analytical intelligence did not find much scope since principles were buried deeply below the pyramid of fact. So long as a catalogue of the materials in the world we know was the chief requirement, necessarily the chief requirement if the data upon which science was to be built were to be known, the memorising mind aided by more or less analytical ability was the best type of scientific mind. When the catalogue of material was tolerably completed, the memory became less and the analytical faculty more important. Many of the great chemists of the 19th century were wonderful memorisers and knew accurately vast numbers of isolated facts. Their powers of mental analysis were often not great and did not need to be, since among the hosts of new facts only a few superficial connecting threads were at first to be expected. The 20th century has seen something of a submergence of the type of mind characteristic of the illustrious 19th-century chemists, and the physicist with comparatively little comprehensive knowledge of fact dominates science. He penetrates deeply at one place into the pyramid of fact, and from the nterior suddenly discovers comprehensive webs of theory woven through the entire pyramid.

These visions suggest new techniques for the cataloguing and synthesising chemists. The initiative has passed to the analytical from the memorising part of the intelligence. Consequently the scientific geniuses of to-day tend to be famous before the age of twenty-five. Heisenberg and Dirac, the present leaders of theoretical physics, are both about 30 years of age.

XXII

COMPOUNDS OF ATOMS

SPACE-TIME could be conceived as empty of matter but containing travelling radiation—light, cosmic rays, etc. Then the radiation might for some reason congeal itself into parcels of equal quantities of protons and electrons. Such a universe would know at first only these two substances, familiar to us as the nuclei of hydrogen atoms, and free electrons. If the protons and electrons were not mixed, there would be a proton gas and an electron gas. The universe would know of no state of matter except the gaseous, because the powerful electrical charges on the protons would keep them all apart, and so too with the electrons in their electron-gas. If some of the protons and electrons came together, they might pair off to form complete hydrogen atoms, i.e., nuclei with an attendant electron. The electric charges on the proton and electron being equal and opposite, there would be no field of electric force beyond the atom's vicinity, and it would be able to approach other atoms very closely without being repelled. Since an atom of hydrogen contains only one each of two dissimilar kinds of particle, it is not a symmetrical object. Two atoms together would make a more symmetrical arrangement. They should therefore be expected to combine into molecules, i.e., small groups of atoms more symmetrical than individual atoms. The idea is suggested purely schematically in the figure:

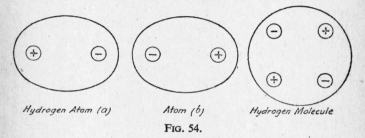

Hydrogen Atom (a)   Atom (b)   Hydrogen Molecule

FIG. 54.

Molecules of atoms and compounds though without a total electric charge have secondary fields around them due to lack of symmetry. These secondary fields exert their effect but often are interrupted and overshadowed by other forces. For instance, molecules of hydrogen will cohere together if not interfered with. But if heated and caused to vibrate, they ultimately shake so violently that the cohering force is countered. The molecules roll over each other, still exhibiting some cohesion, but as the temperature rises the vibrations increase until this slight cohesion is quite overcome by the intense shaking of the molecules, which now fly about violently and bump against each other, rebounding with a force much greater than the cohesive attraction they experience during the bump. The hydrogen exists therefore in three states, of strong, weak and no cohesion, and is manifested as a solid, liquid and gas. Matter is manifested in these three states.

Since molecules are structures of definite and various forms their natural times of vibration are variable as with bells of varying shape and size. Molecules are caused to vibrate when rays of light fall on them.

Sometimes they pick up the vibration and hand it on unchanged to their neighbours; then the substance made out of the molecules is transparent. Sometimes the molecules respond to only one wavelength of light, say that of red light; then the substance is transparent to red light only. Hence the colours of many materials depend on the structure of their molecules. The compounds of the metal chromium are often of brilliant colour: chromatic, hence the metal's name. Aniline dyes belong to a group of substances whose molecules have a tendency to be limited in their resonance with visible light, causing them to possess brilliant colours.

A universe containing molecules and a sufficiently low temperature for them to combine offers immensely various possibilities. If the temperature is about 2,500° C. and pressure 15 lb. per square inch there is a possibility of existence for a few solids, the metal tungsten, for example. At 1,500° C. and the same pressure a number of liquids would be possible, molten iron, lava, glass, etc. At 500° C. and 15 lb. per square inch pressure there would be a considerable range of solids and liquids, though not a very useful one, for substances retaining their constitution at that temperature are fairly stable and therefore not swift to change. The world at 500° C. would be a hot but slow place. At 100° C. the number of possible solids and liquids would have increased greatly. Between 100° C. and 0° C. the range of solids and liquids would have increased enormously. Below 0° C. the range of state would decrease. There would be many solids but fewer liquids and at —100° C. the liquids would become rare. At —200° C. proportion of gases to solids would be of the same order as the proportion of solids to gases at 2,000° C. At —273° C. the whole world would be solid and liquids and gases unknown, a condition parallel to that at 3,000° C. and 15 lb. per square inch pressure, when all the world would be gaseous.

Thus the world between 0° C.–100° C. when at a

pressure of 15 lb. per square inch pressure presents the largest variety of states of substances. The possibilities of compounding and mixing molecules between that temperature range are at a maximum. If nature desired to practise complicated chemistry she would tend to choose to work in a laboratory within that range of temperature.

XXIII

CHEMISTRY OF CARBON COMPOUNDS

As nature increased the variety of the universe by condensing together collections of protons and electrons, she produced at least eighty-nine different shapes and arrangements of groups; the elements helium, lithium, boron, carbon, nitrogen, . . . iron cobalt, radium, uranium. This assortment of eighty-nine contributed to the variety of existences, and further groups among the ninety (adding the original hydrogen proton to the list) produced that vast range of substances immediately familiar as matter, water, air, sugar, wood, iron and all the materials of common experience. Among the eighty-nine groupings of protons and electrons there was the substance carbon. Its atom contained a nucleus of twelve protons and six electrons, with six electrons revolving in the outer region of the atom. There was an outer shell of four and an inner shell of two electrons. The outer shell has half the complete electron shell number of eight.

That atoms with, 2, 8, 16 or 32 electrons in their outer shells are peculiarly inert and do not combine with other atom, has been explained. So a pair of carbon atoms would together have eight electrons in their outer electron shells, presenting a unit with certain tendencies to stability. Carbon atoms have a unique property of sticking together in chains or rings. The physical explanation is not yet clear, but the researches of Lennard-Jones, Hückel and others suggest this unique property is deducible from the special arrangement of the protons and electrons in the carbon atom. The fact that the two sets of four outer electrons add

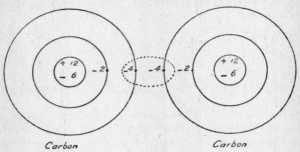

Fig. 55.

up to one set of eight when two carbon atoms are very close together probably has something to do with it.

The four vacancies in the outer electron shell give

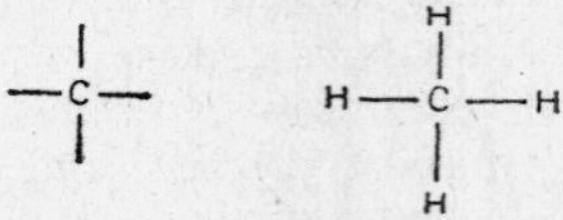

$$-\overset{\displaystyle |}{\underset{\displaystyle |}{C}}-\qquad\qquad H-\overset{\displaystyle H}{\underset{\displaystyle H}{C}}-H$$

Fig. 56

carbon a valency of four. Four hydrogen atoms (which have one electron in their electron shell) will normally combine with one of carbon (fig. 56).

Due to the property of carbon atoms being able partially to satisfy or saturate themselves, the following arrangement is possible:

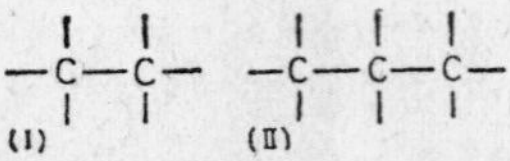

$$-\overset{|}{\underset{|}{C}}-\overset{|}{\underset{|}{C}}-\qquad -\overset{|}{\underset{|}{C}}-\overset{|}{\underset{|}{C}}-\overset{|}{\underset{|}{C}}-$$
(I)   (II)

Fig. 57.

Any number of carbon atoms can attach themselves in a chain, leaving two or three of each atom's four ties unoccupied, unsaturated as it is termed. Thus chains of two, three, four, twenty carbon atoms can each act as the foundation for a whole series of substances. For instance, a chain of six carbon atoms with all their free ties saturated with hydrogen gives hexane:

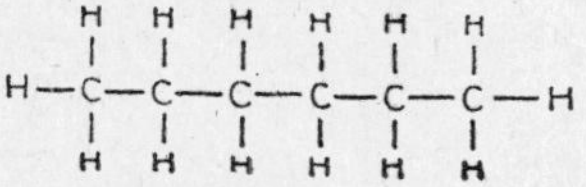

Fig. 58. Hexane.

These hydrogen atoms can be replaced by those of other substances having the requisite number of ties. Evidently the variety of combinations in which the chain of six carbon atoms is the basis is enormous. Chains of varying numbers of carbon atoms are the basis of the vast series of fats, oils and paraffins called aliphatic compounds.

For instance, the chain of two carbon atoms can saturate itself as follows:

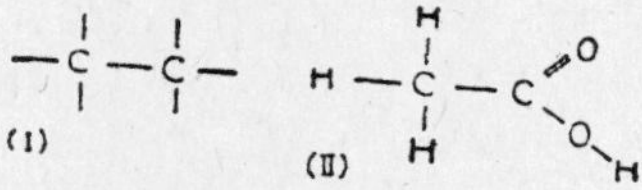

Fig. 59. Acetic Acid.

two free ties of the carbon atom on the left being saturated with one atom of oxygen, and the third free tie by an atom of oxygen attached to an atom of hydrogen. This substance is acetic acid.

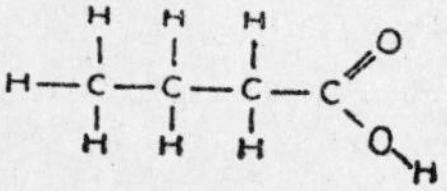

Fig. 60. Butyric Acid.

With four carbon atoms in the chain butyric acid is obtained. This substance gives the characteristic taste to rancid butter. If there are sixteen atoms the substance is palmitic acid, the acid obtainable from palm oil.

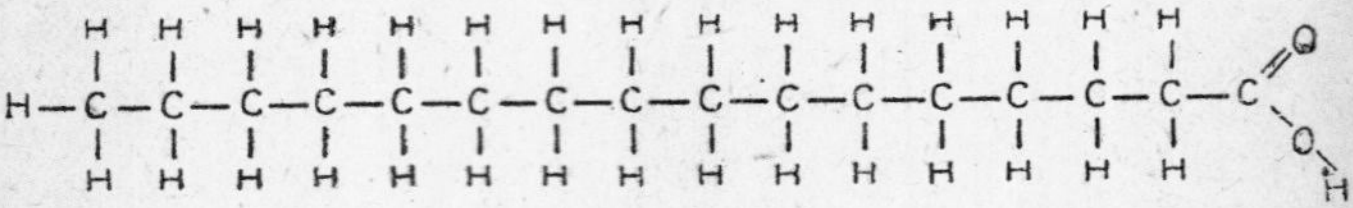

FIG. 61. Palmitic Acid.

Evidently such a molecule must be long and thin, or coiled up if its length is not much greater than its breadth. This is demonstrated by the thin film experiments of Langmuir, Adam and others, where the number of fatty acid molecules in a layer one molecule thick is known, enabling the dimensions of the average molecule to be estimated. It proves to be straight, long and thin, or coiled like a spring, or in other predictable conformations.

If one of the carbon atoms has a free tie saturated by half-satisfied oxygen, another series of substances is formed, the alcohols.

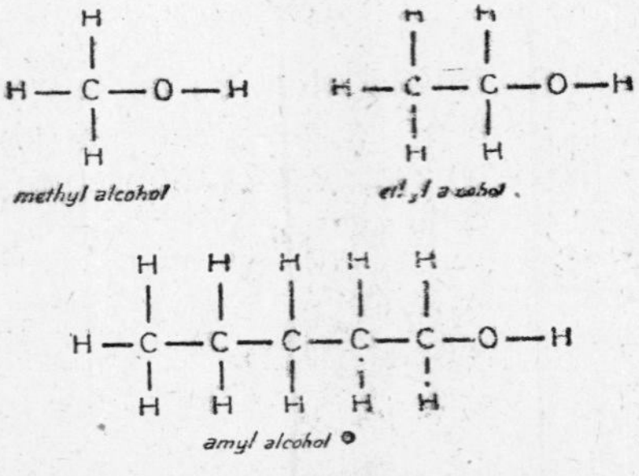

methyl alcohol   ethyl alcohol.

amyl alcohol

FIG. 62.

Since the O–H pair need not necessarily be at the end of the chain of five carbon atoms, several kinds of amyl-alcohol are possible. The composition of all of them is the same, but the structure and properties of each are different. Such substances are called isomers, and the phenomenon isomerism. It adds immensely to the possibilities of variety in the carbon compounds.

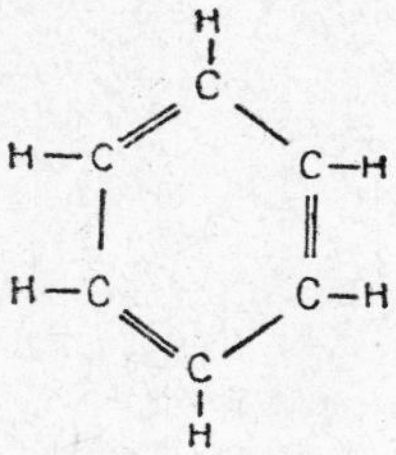

benzene

FIG. 63.

Besides chains of carbon atoms, rings are possible. This structure explains the peculiar property of benzene which behaves in many ways as if all of its carbon atoms were saturated, and yet will accept six more hydrogen atoms.

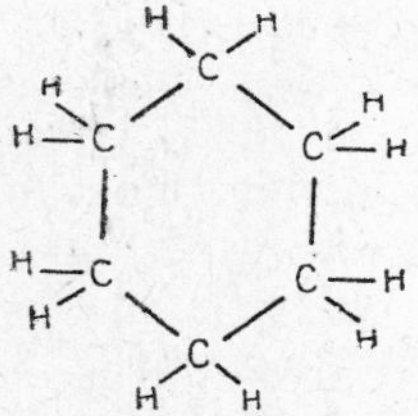

cyclohexane

FIG. 64.

The ring idea was discovered by Kekule, and has had a great influence on civilisation. The series of aromatic substances (taking their title from aromatic oils) are based on the ring of six carbon atoms. Aniline dyes, many explosives and drugs are built around rings of carbon atoms, and this insight into their structure has suggested how they might be synthesised.

The ring need not consist entirely of carbon atoms. A nitrogen atom may satisfy three free carbon ties as follows:

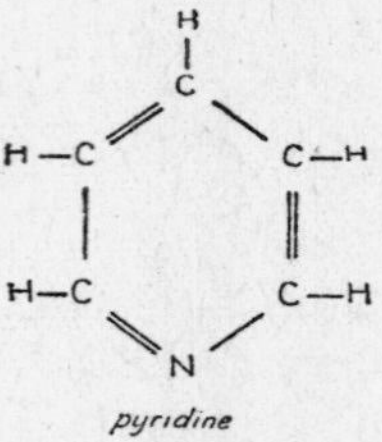

pyridine

FIG. 65.

forming the substance pyridine.

This extraordinary reactive property of carbon atoms enables innumerable substances of slowly grading properties to be built up. About 1,000,000 carbon compounds are known and perhaps 500,000 of them have been artificially synthesised in the laboratory. These and perhaps many more are the raw material nature utilises in manufacturing living organisms.

The sort of inbreeding tendency of carbon atoms probably depends on their structure. When this is elucidated, possibly another substance with similar structure but different constitution could be synthesised, as ionised helium is an analogue with hydrogen. Presumably a new family of inbreeding substances would be synthesisable, another million compounds of finely graded properties. Would a new kind of life be evolvable out of these, an X-life as it were, corresponding to our present "carbon-life"?

XXIV

WHAT CAN BE DONE WITH SOLID, LIQUID AND GASEOUS COMPOUNDS

WHEN the right temperature for the existence of multifarious solids, liquids and gases occurred in the Universe, what happened ?

An intense activity among carbon compounds. Chains and rings of carbon atoms proliferated and exchanged enumerable molecules among the free ties, the unsaturated valencies, of the carbon atoms in the rings. By incessant mixture and simmering the compounds became more and more complicated. Mixtures kept up a steady state of interchange and motion, and the innumerable internal reactions gradually reached a degree of complication which conferred on the mixture a stability something like that of a spinning top, which when disturbed tends to return to its former state of motion. When the quantity of the mixture accumulated beyond a limit it became unstable and split into two pieces which began to suck in more materials from the environment until once more the interacting whorl of liquids and materials became over-big and split again. In some such way, perhaps, nature achieved the subtler syntheses of molecular substances.

Aeons later an outcome of these earlier syntheses began to try synthesising on its own. Man mixed substances together under unusual conditions and hoped that something good would come of it. Immediately after discovering the idea of synthesis he tried to synthesise God ; since influence with an Omnipotency would be very useful. The medicine man of savage tribes at once tried that great experiment and always attempted to convince his fellows of his success. Later, in the Middle Ages, he restricted himself to the synthesis of homunculi, little men to be produced complete in laboratory crucibles.

The alchemists in the end had to relinquish this high aim. By A.D. 1800 men were pleased if they could analyse or synthesise even the simplest new compound. In 1828 they were thrilled when Wohler synthesised for the first time a substance found only in connection with living organisms, urea. What are the synthetic prospects now ?

The nitrogen of the air can be combined with hydrogen obtained from water-gas, a mixture of carbon monoxide and hydrogen obtained by heating together air, steam and coke. The ammonia so compounded can be combined into nitrates capable of doubling or more the fertility of the world's agriculture. The major worker in this achievement is Haber, the great German physical chemist.

Water-gas can be produced cheaply in extremely large quantities. From it formaldehyde is easily synthesised, and from formaldehyde the lower sugars, some of which are edible. Thus coke, steam, and air are a possible source of food.

The simple gas methane is also easily obtainable from water-gas. From methane, benzene and acetylene can be synthesised, and these are the bases of motor fuels.

From coal, lubricating oils, lamp oils and fuel oils can be obtained by treating it with hydrogen under high pressure. The hydrogen combines with the coal and produces liquid compounds from which these can be separated. As soon as the natural oil resources of the world are too exhausted to be worked economically these synthetic oils will be manufactured commercially on a vast scale.

The exhaustion of coal and oil by no means limits the vision of chemists, as Professor Donnan has remarked.

In the world are vast deposits of limestone and chalk. These are the shells of dead marine organisms which accumulated in their myriad skeletons a huge store of carbon. By heat carbon dioxide is easily obtained from limestone. Heat and electricity are easily obtained from water-power, so there is no difficulty in decomposing the limestone for carbon dioxide, or water for hydrogen. From these, sugar and fuel are synthesisable, and the equivalent of bread drawn from stones.

Harington has synthesised thyroxin, the active substance of the thyroid gland in the neck. A deficiency of activity in the thyroid gland causes a man to be deficient mentally and physically (Plate XVI).

With the future synthesis of other important principles in gland extracts, a series of very potent new drugs is placed in man's hands.

One of the important substances called vitamines has been synthesised. If ergosterol, one of the components of the fat found in animals, is treated with ultra-violet rays, Vitamine D is produced. Apparently the value of cucumbers as fresh vegetables is partly due to the vitamines they contain. These have been produced by the effect of sunlight containing ultra-violet rays on the substances in the cucumber. If sunshine produced cucumber vitamines, then man has only to unlock cucumber vitamines to produce sunlight. He has only to make the reaction go the other way. There is nothing inconceivable in that. Swift's notorious gibe on the fantastic attempts of scientists to obtain sunbeams from cucumbers seems to be receiving an unexpected and triumphant rejoinder.

XXV

COLLOIDS

AN atom is a comparatively symmetrical object, but molecules formed by the combination of atoms generally are not. Molecules are frequently dumb-bell shaped, and sometimes exist in the form of a string of atoms beaded together. The string may be coiled or straight or bent. Since molecules are often dumb-bell shaped their properties at the opposite ends may be different. At some distance from the molecule, only an average

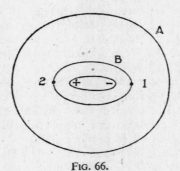

Fig. 66.

effect is noticed, but in the neighbourhood of the ends the effects will be different.

In a molecule the positive and negative electric forces are equal, so a particle on boundary A would experience no electric force, but a particle on boundary B would experience a negative field in position (1) and a positive in position (2). When substances are in contact, as, for example, two liquids, the molecules of one can come into actual contact with molecules of the other. The local charges on the ends of the molecules may cause the substances to have a partial affinity for each other. For instance, if alcohol is poured into water, a perfect mixture is formed. If benzene is poured on water it collects together in a large drop and will not mix. Some substances do not mix properly with water and yet cannot be described as being entirely immiscible. When poured on to water they spread over the surface if unconstrained until there is a surface layer of molecules.

Though the molecules as wholes refuse to mix with water, one of their ends may. Thus it is possible to have rows of molecules standing like soldiers on parade over the water's surface. Evidently the behaviour of

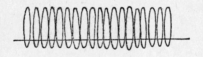

FIG 67.

the particular molecules in contact may not be characteristic of the mixture of substances as a whole. There will be a special condition at the surfaces where the two liquids mix which will not be characteristic of the general properties of the mixture.

A beautiful demonstration of this point is given by an experiment made in Prof. H. Freundlich's laboratory. Water and benzene do not mix. If portions of these liquids are poured into a tube, the benzene floats on the water. A small quantity of the colourless base of the dye rhodamine—O is added, and this dissolves in the benzene. If the surface between the benzene and water is closely examined it is seen to be slightly pink. The condition at the surface is sufficiently peculiar to decompose the base into the pink dye. If the tube is shaken violently the contents become bright pink. The commotion greatly extends the area of the surfaces of

contact between the water and benzene so the amount
of dye base decomposed is sufficiently increased to
colour the mass of the mixture.

The partial forces acting in surfaces due to the
different reaction from different parts of the same
molecule assist in a very large and important class of
phenomena, i.e., in those of substances containing very
great areas of surface between two constituents. A pure
liquid, solid or gas is made of molecules so small and
uniform that it may be regarded as a continuous medium.
Suppose a cubic inch of gold is dropped into such a
medium. It drops to the bottom. The area of the gold
is six square inches. Suppose the cube is subdivided
into little cubes of edge a millionth of an inch. There
will be 1,000,000,000,000,000,000 of them, and their
area will be 6,000,000 square inches or about one acre.
The effect of this subdivision is to increase enormously
the area of the gold in contact with the molecules of
water. Since the molecules of water are all in motion
they are able perpetually to exert their bumps over an
area of an acre, and yet the gold in that area weighs an
ounce only. The pressure on the gold is sufficient to
counteract the effect of gravity on it, so the particles
of gold never settle to the bottom of the liquid. In fact,
they cause the water to appear a permanent ruby red.
This suspension of gold in water is probably the "potable
gold" of the alchemists, and was rediscovered by
Faraday.

Since colloidal particles are variable in size between
certain limits they are enormously more complicated
in behaviour than simple atoms and molecules. If a
colloid is magnified so that its particles are visible, all
are seen to differ in size, though to lie between limits.
They resemble a crowd of humans in the small variation
in gross size combined with enormous variation in
detail. In fact, the complication of colloids is a large
advance towards the complication necessary to support
life in matter (Plates XVII and XVIII).

evident. The colloids are the root from which living processes have grown.

The exact steps of evolution from colloid to living particle are not yet known as the evolution from proton and electron to colloid is known, and the evolution from simple living cell to man is surmised.

Lately Professor Svedberg of Upsala has made some interesting discoveries about the colloids in matter from living organisms. He obtains colloidal solutions of substances such as ovalbumin, hæmoglobin, legumin, etc., and whirls them round in his ultra-centrifuge. This instrument consists essentially of a steel wheel revolved by a turbine driven by high-pressure oil. Rates of rotation up to 45,000 per minute are obtainable. The centrifugal force on particles placed in an experimental cavity in the wheel goes up to 125,000 times that of gravity. Thus a particle weighing one gram will have exerted on it a force equal to 125,000 grams weight when placed in the wheel and rotated at full speed. Thus the ultra-centrifuge enables in effect the force of gravity to be increased 125,000 times. Since sedimentation is due to gravity causing fine particles in liquids to settle, and colloidal solutions are characterised by the property of their suspended particles of withstanding sedimentation, as previously explained; colloidal solutions ought to sediment if subjected to the equivalent of an enormous increase in the strength of gravity. That is what Prof. Svedberg finds. When colloidal solutions are placed in his ultra-centrifuge they are subjected to the equivalent of an 125,000-fold increase of gravity. Each article in the solution is pulled down to the bottom with a force 125,000 times as great as when the solution is standing quietly in a test tube on the bench, subjected to the sedimenting force of gravity only. By finding the rate at which colloidal solutions sediment in the ultra-centrifuge Prof. Svedberg can estimate the mass of the colloidal particles in them. He finds that all the different kinds of colloidal particles obtained from living matter with which he has experimented weigh 34,500 (taking the weight of the oxygen atom as 16) or two, three, six or more times that number. His experiments suggest that a particle of molecular weight 34,500 is the unit out of which living matter is constructed. Perhaps the structure of living matter is enormously simpler than we in humility have assumed, the complexity of structure arising not from the variety of the units used but from the ingenuity with which they are put together. (See Plate XIX.)

Professor Svedberg's remarkable number 34,500 has arisen in some beautiful researches recently made by Mr. W. T. Astbury on the structure of hairs, fibres, horns and animal nails. By X-ray analysis Astbury has shown that keratin, the basic material out of which all animal (and human) hairs, horns and nails are made, can exist in two forms, the a and the β forms. In the a-form the molecules of the keratin are arranged in an elastic shape. Hairs made out of a-keratin are elastic, but if they are subjected to heat and strain they turn into β-keratin, which is inelastic. "Permanent waving" is an empirical technique for turning a into β-keratin. The reverse process occurs when β-keratin is changed into the a-form. Inelastic keratin such as nails and horns is in the β-form. We all know how our toe-nails are apt to tear after a bath. This is due to the keratin changing from the β to the a form: our nails temporarily become more like hairs. There is little difference between hairs and nails and horns in constitution, only in structure.

It is interesting to observe that nature discovered the art of "permanent waving" aeons ago, for the coiled horns of animals are merely "permanent waves." The stiff coils of a ram's horns are made of β-keratin. If the horn is subjected to suitable treatment its keratin changes to the a-form and becomes elastic, and the "permanent waves" may be steamed out.

Astonishing as this X-ray investigation of the nature of "permanent waves" has proved, there is a further item of exciting information. Astbury finds that the molecules of keratin making up hairs and horns are of about 34,500 molecular weight. The unit Svedberg had found appearing in an entirely different kind of investigation! Ultra-centrifuges and X-rays seem to point to the same weight of unit in the structure of living matter.

XXVI

FILTRABLE VIRUSES

COLLOIDS often show properties remarkably similar to those of matter in living organisms, but no colloid made from dead matter even once alive, has ever been found capable of reproducing itself. In spite of their subtleties and complications none has been made capable of that, though in the future perhaps one will be made in the laboratory. There are entities associated with organisms we should certainly regard as living which themselves can scarcely be labelled alive or dead. Perhaps they may be considered nearer to life, not because they are more life- than dead-like, but because they are apparently associated always with living things. They are the famous filtrable viruses, the unseen tiny entities, smaller than bacilli or bacteria, the causes or the effects of certain diseases such as measles, foot and mouth disease, rabies, infantile paralysis, cattle-pneumonia.

They are invisible in all microscopes using ordinary light, but can be partially photographed in Barnard's ultra-violet ray microscope. The limits of microscopic power are given by the wave-length of light, objects substantially smaller than the light used in the attempt to reveal them remain invisible. Since the wavelength of ultra-violet rays is less than that of visible light it is capable of revealing ultra-microscopic objects to a photographic plate if not to the human eye which works only with visible light. The transparency of virus organisms increases the difficulty of examining them by light. In some cases they can be plated with molecules of gold, which is opaque, rendering their outline more revealable.

In fig. 70 the sequence of development of the filtrable virus associated with cattle-pneumonia is seen. Barnard pieces it together from many separate photographs. This entity seems to exist normally in the form of a tiny ball. It swells up and little protuberances appear on the outer surface. These wander off at the end of fine threads and begin to swell and produce their own nodules, and so on. This process of development is very unusual. No other entity reproduces quite like that.

The fact that viruses do reproduce is perhaps enough to establish that they are living organisms. But they do not show many of the properties of living organisms, or at least these properties have not yet been observed. They have never been observed to respire. If they consumed oxygen like other living organisms they would produce carbon dioxide, but no experimental attempt to detect carbon dioxide respired from viruses has succeeded. Possibly the quantities produced are too small to be detected, or the experimental difficulties are too great, as they might well be in trying to detect respiration in organisms too small to be seen.

No virus has been discovered apart from the animal or plant which it characteristically inhabits, nor is there convincing evidence they can be cultivated artificially. They develop quickly enough in their natural environment. The foot-and-mouth disease virus will always grow in the blister-fluid of cows. If it is taken out of

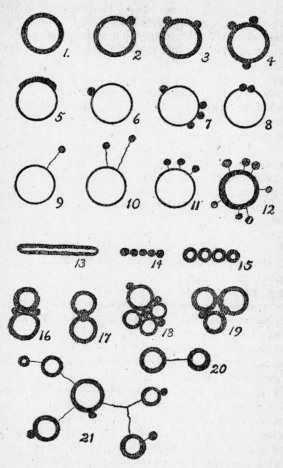

FIG. 70. (After Barnard).

the fluid it does not grow, though it retains the possibility for a long time. As soon as it is put back into cow-blister fluid it begins to grow again. Possibly bacteriologists have not yet discovered the suitable artificial fluid in which the virus will multiply, but so far there is no good evidence the virus will multiply except in the blister-fluid.

The viruses seem to multiply only in the presence of young growing cells, and possibly only while their specific effect persists, i.e., the virus multiplies only while the animal is becoming increasingly ill. Professor Boycott considers that though the fact of virus multiplication is plain, there is no certain proof of the similarity of the process to that of breeding in bacilli or bacteria. If so much virus is put into the animal, more can be taken out, but he does not consider it proved that the increase are necessarily descendants of the originals. They may be new ones generated in the interaction between the introduced virus and the young growing cells with which they are invariably associated. Possibly the viruses are parts of these young cells come adrift, limbs of them, as it were, partly alive and yet not complete living organisms capable of self-reproduction in any suitable and not one particular environment. If this were so, their peculiar semi-life-like properties would be explained.

The filtrable viruses associated with well-known diseases in ourselves and domestic animals have naturally drawn attention.

There appear to be viruses associated not with diseases of large animals but with the microbes, the bacteria and bacilli causing these diseases. The microbes have their own diseases and viruses are associated with these, and called bacteriophage. The nature of these preyers on bacteria is even more obscure than the filter passers causing foot-and-mouth and other large animal diseases. Bacteriophage is supposed to be the agent which arises sometimes in a harmless or deadly culture of bacteria, and epidemically wipes them out, destroying the destroyer.

Bacteriophage seems to be limited even more than the animal-disease viruses. It multiplies only in the presence of the bacilli it attacks, and many workers believe it is produced by the bacilli, though it can be transferred after being formed from culture to culture.

Its behaviour may be considered in parallel with those substances produced by damaged cells. When a man cuts his finger the cells about the wound produce something which stimulates the growth of the new tissue. The amount produced is proportional to the amount of damage done.

This something stimulates the growth and hence increases the quantity of tissue. The increase in quantity of tissue means that when the tissue decays still more of the entity will be produced. In a way the substance or thing can multiply itself indirectly. Yet no one has regarded it as being alive.

What is to be thought of the agent or virus which produces cancers in fowls? Rous discovered that a solution could be obtained from these tumours in which there was nothing to be seen or cultivated and yet produced cancers on fowls into which it had been inoculated. This agent does not multiply or is not produced apart from the cancers, and it retains its activity after being severely purified.

It is not unlike those substances called catalysts and enzymes which stimulate chemical reactions. Hydrogen and nitrogen will combine to form ammonia in the presence of a mixture of iron oxide and other substances. Starch is converted into sugar by the ptylain present in saliva. These substances are not alive, yet they show a lively power of stimulating reactions. Like living organisms they are often rendered inactive by substances such as chloroform.

One virus or agent can be made quite straightforwardly from normal tissue. If a filtered solution is made from the testis of a rabbit and inoculated into the testis of another rabbit, this testis often develops an inflammation. If a filtrate is made from the inflammation and inoculated into other rabbits, these develop the inflammation, which can be passed on indefinitely. When the rabbits recover they are found to be immune to the disease, for fresh inoculation leaves them unaffected. This agent, which behaves rather like a virus, seems almost within the scope of manufacture.

Will scientists discover how to produce entities having some of the properties of life from studies of the nature of these viruses which seem partly alive and partly dead ? Possibly. They may prove to be the clue to some of the missing links between matter and organism.

XXVII

BACTERIA

THE smallest living things of which much is known are the bacteria. They are surprisingly important in spite of their size. If the process of evolution from matter to mammal has been long and has passed through the bacterial level of organisation, the latter has not been discarded. Possibly many other links or stages between matter and viruses and bacteria have utterly disappeared, making the evolution more difficult to discover, but bacteria themselves have been retained and given a very great part in the economy of living organisms.

These tiny organisms are usually about one twenty-five-thousandth of an inch in diameter and about six times as long. Their appearance is very simple. They look like a small rod and in that case are called bacilli. If round they are called cocci, and if wriggling, spirilli.

In many cases nothing but plain rods or blobs can be seen. There is no obvious internal structure, and yet the entities are alive. Their contents must be of a kind sufficiently complicated to support life. The wrigglers have hairs on them which lash about and propel them through the containing fluid.

They breed at an immense rate, about once every half-hour. If the whole of a single bacterium's progeny could be kept alive, it would total 281,476,587,353,856 members by the end of one day.

Besides a certain variation in shape, some bacteria have a characteristic group life. They grow in long chains, sometimes with the chains adjacent to form a mosaic or mat. (See fig. 71.)

These characteristic groupings show great differences, but very many quite different species appear identical to the observer with his present microscope equipment. The species are distinguished by their effects, for of two species otherwise apparently identical, one may be deadly to animals and the other of great practical value for preparing human food.

Bacteria breed in the simplest manner. They just grow until they have reached a certain size and age, and then split in half, two bacteria being where there was one before. The process is descriptively as simple as that. Of course, if it could be examined minutely it would probably be discovered to be very complicated. There is no sexual machinery whatever. Reproduction in bacteria requires no separate sexes. This is philo-sophically interesting, for it seems to suggest that in the deepest analysis sex is not the most fundamental requirement in the mechanism of reproduction. It has evolved as a refinement with great possibilities and prob-ably other purposes on the plain basis of reproduction by splitting into two.

The bacteria have a second powerful quality which helps them to survive. When conditions are adverse they temporarily change their nature, becoming tough and quiescent. In this second state they are described as having formed themselves into spores. These are extraordinarily resistant to an inimical environment. Even in steam of 30 lb. per square inch and at 120° C. they often retain their vitality for a quarter of an hour.

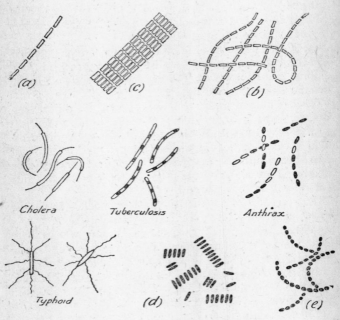

Cholera   Tuberculosis   Anthrax

Typhoid   (d)   (e)

Fig. 71. (After Wells, Huxley, Wells.)

In ordinary boiling water they may survive for hours. To be sure medical instruments are sterilised, they have to be exposed to moist super-heated steam in an auto-clave, an apparatus devised for the purpose.

They resist extreme cold even more remarkably.

After six months in liquid air at — 190° C. they have been found to retain their vitality, and in undisturbed rest they survive for years. An organism which reproduces once in half an hour and while active is comparatively vulnerable, for boiling swiftly kills active bacteria, can change itself into a spore sleeping as it were for a period sufficient for thousands of generations of normal life. An active bacterium lives through about 50 generations in a day. A year sees 20,000 of its generations. If man could quiesce under adverse circumstances for a proportionate time the period would be about 1,000,000 years. He could pass all that time in waiting for the suitable environment to return. Thus the power of this quality of resistance in bacteria is very great. They may be floating in this dormant condition in the air, in food, even in icebergs and hailstones. As soon as they fall into a suitable environment, such as a sore throat for diphtheria, an unclean water-supply for cholera, warm blood in the veins of animals and men for anthrax, the dormancy ends and the bacteria reproduce vigorously. Others require apparently most unpromising substances for a necessary part of their respiration. Ammonia, free nitrogen from the air, sulphuretted hydrogen (the gas from bad eggs) are examples of peculiar substitutes or additions to the oxygen used by all other living organisms. These properties give bacteria their extraordinary power. They can accomplish the oddest tasks, turning fruit juice into wine, milk into butter and cheese, enrich the soil and poison animals and men.

The diphtheria bacillus flourishes in the human throat. During its life it emits a substance into the environing fluid which permeates into the blood stream. This substance is a poison and attacks the heart. But it also has a permanent effect on the patient's blood, for if the patient recovers his blood is found to have been left by this poison in a resistant condition so that a second discharge from a second attack has no effect: the person has become immune. His blood seems to have been given a permanent quality inimical to the poison emitted by the diphtheria bacillus. In fact, his blood can be used as an aggressive agent. If a few drops are pricked out of him and mixed with the poison collected from a diphtheria colony, another person having the mixture injected into him will not suffer any harm. This is fortunate and strange. The poison can exist quite independently of the bacillus, which is easily demonstrated by filtering out bacilli from a culture and injecting the fluid into a suitable animal when the diptheria symptoms will be exhibited even if the animal has no sore throat.

A subject recovered from diphtheria appears to have a chemical substance in his blood capable of neutralising the diphtheria poison. The immunity conferred on a patient after recovery from typhoid fever operates in a different way. A few drops of this blood seems to have the power of causing the typhoid bacilli in a test-tube culture solution to coagulate and quiesce.

The operation of the bacteria which consume the lungs and cause "consumption" seems to depend on the condition of the patient. Nearly everyone contains consumption bacilli, but the bacillus does not flourish in him unless his body is susceptible. The exact cause of susceptibility is unknown, but associated in many cases with poor bodily condition; lack of nourishment and exercise, or weakness after an attack of pneumonia or some other illness. The bacillus itself is a tough one and difficult to kill.

The rate at which bacilli multiply ought to cause them to show changes in heredity. If man can evolve from some kind of ape in 100,000 generations, possibly bacilli might evolve new species in periods of years. Of course, the bacteria are so comparatively simple that there is not much scope for alterations in constitution, but the rapid succession of generations should utmostly exploit such as there is. Some direct evidence is in favour of the evolution of new species of bacteria. For instance, in recent years sleepy sickness has become a deadly infection. It was unknown or unrecognised in Europe twelve years ago. Perhaps the bacillus has evolved quickly or mutated ("mutation" is discussed later) from some other harmless species only since the beginning of the twentieth century.

Syphilis apparently changed from a tiresome into a dangerous infection in the fifteenth century.

The evils due to bacteria have received more attention than the goods. Their contribution to well-being is prodigious and varied. Some bacteria are capable of living in the dark entirely on chemicals, without even the assistance of sunlight. These bacteria can produce life out of the indisputably dead. This fact suggests a bacterium may have been the first kind of organism to evolve from dead matter, for it could not live on itself and all other was purely dead matter. That is one justification for regarding bacteria or some organism of that sort as the link between dead and living matter. Another kind of bacteria can eat bricks. It is found in decaying stone, and perhaps is a type of organism which helped to manufacture soil in the Earth's youth. There is evidence that soil is made by these bacteria on barren rocks and mountain peaks.

Everyone knows peas, beans, lupins and other similar plants, and the important use of them in agriculture. Thousands of years ago agriculturalists discovered that an occasional crop of these plants enriched the soil if ploughed in without reaping. About 1880 this effect was carefully studied. Land had these crops cultivated on it for fifteen years in succession, then the soil was analysed. It contained three times more nitrogen than at the beginning. The plants had some power of taking the inert nitrogen out of the air and fixing it in the soil. When these plants were examined the well-known

nodules on their roots in particular were carefully
studied.

If the plants were grown in sterilised soil with additional
chemicals, no nodules appeared on them and instead of
increasing the nitrate content of the soil, required extra
nitrate as one of the chemical additions to keep them
alive. The plants themselves were not different from
other green plants in being unable to take nitrogen from
the air, they could achieve that only with the assistance
of the nodules. When people have lumps on them they
are usually supposed to be ill, or at least, infected. Could
the lupins be ill, and the cause of the illness be the power
which took the nitrogen from the air and fixed it in the
soil ? Study revealed the bacteria in the nodules were
storing nitrogen from the air, and when the nodules
were plou hed into the soil, provided the refresher of
nitrate.

Other kinds of bacteria have indirectly helped to
create not agricultural, but industrial civilisation. These
use iron-rust or manganese in the construction of their
cell-walls, and have produced accumulations of bog-iron
ore, ochre, and manganese ores, subsequently to be
turned into paint and bicycles and innumerable very
inorganic objects.

No sight is more significant than the side of a hole in
a field. The depth of life on the Earth is seen to be
extraordinarily shallow, not more than a few dozen
inches. The Earth is 8,000 miles in diameter; life
penetrates perhaps eight feet into its surface. The
precariousness of life, the green veil cosmically diaphan-
ous, is revealed.

Every year the Earth rears a new growth of plants
and animals. This has been repeated for centuries and
millions of years. Why is there no great thickness of
organic débris ? Because bacteria decompose it before
it accumulates uncomfortably. The hard part of
plants is mainly cellulose, the material of the walls of the
plant's cells. This is consumed by certain bacteria

and its constituents freed from combination, so the
accumulation of plant débris never grows beyond a
comparatively small quantity. During the process
methane and sulphuretted hydrogen are released from
the cellulose by bacteria, and the former is well known
as marsh-gas, which arises from the active bacteria in
the woody débris of marshes. Sulphuretted hydrogen is
recognised in the wind issuing from animals during
digestion, and from humans whose digestive apparatus
is not working properly. Horses especially belch
wind. They live on grass containing much cellulose.
Bacteria in their large intestine decomposes the
cellulose into substances from which the horses can
derive nourishment, for cellulose cannot be directly
digested by horses or humans. Much methane is
produced in the intestine by the bacteria and issues
as wind.

Bacteria are alive and the site of continuous chemical
reactions and hence of evolution of heat. It is they that
help to fire haystacks by "spontaneous combustion".
They live in the hay and reduce it into fine fibres and
powders very susceptible to chemical reaction with
oxygen. When this happens the stack takes fire. Piles
of cotton waste are also sometimes fired through bacterial
action. This has been proved by sterilising waste, and
attempting to make it fire spontaneously. It will not.
If a little fresh waste is added it may, since the bacteria
in it spread to the sterilised part of the pile and multiply,
if the conditions are favourable.

Eating bricks, collecting iron ore, burning haystacks,
poisoning humanity, digesting grass; what a bacterial
repertoire!—and there are other major turns besides.
Some good fish and most bad glows in the dark. The
explanation of the shining is not yet known, but it is
associated with bacterial action. Butcher's meat also
frequently glows in the dark after two days in a cool
room. When treated with a dilute salt solution the
phosphorescence is increased.

Many bacteria including dangerous species are killed or tamed by light. Anthrax and typhus spores which resist severe treatment are killed by suitable exposure to sunlight. The rays beyond the violet, the invisible ultra-violet are the most bactericidal and these can be produced artificially by various kinds of electric lamps. Even when the rays do not kill the bacteria they frequently enervate them and reduce their virulence. The bacterial rôle in the production of butter, cheese, alcholic drinks, perfumes, tobacco, etc., must be mentioned. The subtle flavours of these commodities and luxuries are due to various bacteria, and cheese is itself a mass of bacterial bodies. The most perfect flavours are produced by particular bacteria, and the manufacturer must be careful to encourage these bacteria in his manufacturing processes. For butter and cheese it is possible to isolate some of these desirable bacteria and culture them artificially. If the raw material is deficient in them or does not help their growth they can be added independently. These manufacturers ensure a fine and reliable flavour in their products. The bacteria responsible for defects such as rancidity in butter and ropiness in milk are studied that they may be avoided.

Many of the rarer sensations of life are due to the bacteria, many odours and perfumes and flavours. The deep sensation of health and profundity in things felt in the air of freshly-tilled fields on a spring morning is partly due to the odours produced by bacteria in the soil and released by ploughing. Good tobacco receives its aroma from the activity of bacteria during ripening. The subtleties of innumerable alcoholic drinks are bacterial by-products and for that reason so unapproachable by present chemical synthesis.

Chemists are far from able to make the complicated substances bacteria exude into fermenting juices. Until they are, they cannot make adequate substitutes for wine and the rest. It is practically impossible to remove alcohol from these drinks without damaging the traces of complicated substances which confer all the subtlety on them. Bacteria even undermined the law of nations, since the failure to produce satisfactory substitutes for products qualified by them has shaken the constitution of the United States of America.

END OF VOLUME ONE

GLOSSARY

a-particles : the relatively heavy positively charged particles ejected from certain radioactive substances and proved to be nuclei of atoms of helium.

Angular momentum : A measure of the exertion required to stop the rotation of a rotating body. In a closed system of rotating bodies the amount of exertion from outside required to stop rotation is constant, though inside the system the members may be continually exchanging portions of angular momentum among themselves.

Antitoxin : A substance produced in a body to react against certain poisons.

β-particles : Electrons ejected from radioactive substances.

Colloid : A substance consisting of particles from about 2/10,000ths to 2/10,000,000ths of an inch in diameter strewn through a more or less uniform medium. The particles are too small to behave like grains of sand and not small enough to behave like molecules.

Dominant : When one of the two (from father and mother) factors controlling a hereditary character dominates the other it is said to be dominant.

Dye-base : A fixed group of molecules from which a dye and its variations may be obtained.

Enzyme : One of a group of substances which promotes chemical reactions in the body.

Extra-galactic : Outside the local universe of stars, beyond the Milky Way.

y-rays : Emitted from the nuclei of atoms of radioactive substances, a wave-radiation.

Genes : The factors which carry and control hereditary characters.

Heaviside Layer : A region in the higher atmosphere around the Earth which reflects or bends radio-waves entering it. Its existence was suggested by Oliver Heaviside.

Insulin : An internal secretion which enables the tissues to assimilate sugar; lack of it causes diabetes.

Lymph : A colourless fluid circulating in the bodies of vertebrates.

Molecules : The minimum groups of atoms into which substances can be subdivided.

Mutation : A sport or variety which appears suddenly, due to a change in hereditary constitution.

Nucleus of Atom : The central positively charged particle around which the electrons revolve.

Nucleus of Cell : An essential part of a cell containing the chromosomes and necessary to growth and the mechanism of heredity.

Placenta : The organ through which food and oxygen diffuse from the mother to the embryo in the womb.

Proteins : The fleshy parts of bodies (mainly carbon about 50 per cent., hydrogen about 7 per cent., oxygen about 20 per cent., nitrogen about 20 per cent., sulphur about 2 per cent., and phosphorus about 1 per cent.).

Protoplasm : Living matter, a complex of proteins, the "material basis of life".

Radiation : Energy which is manifested in wavy behaviour. Light, X-rays, ultra-violet rays, cosmic rays, radio-waves, *y*-rays are examples.

Reflessive : One of the two factors governing a hereditary character which is masked by the other (*see Dominant*).

Reflex action : An action determined by the nature of the nervous organisation of the body.

Secretion : Substances produced by glands ; the passing of them into the blood and body.

Thyroid Gland : The "Adam's Apple" in the neck. It secretes thyroxin ($C_{15}H_{11}O_4NI_4$), which affects growth.

Ultra-violet rays : Radiation of wave-length a little less than that of light. Tend to kill bacteria, stimulate growth and are the active principle in photography.

Valency : The number of hooks or bonds which an atom possesses for hitching other atoms; a carbon atom has four.

Vestigial : An organ which appears to have degenerated during evolution; e.g., the tail of the human, vestiges of which exist at the base of the spine.

Vitamin : A substance affecting the efficiency of diet, the absence of which causes rickets, scurvy, etc.

X-rays : *See* Radiation.

PENGUIN BOOKS

FICTION *orange covers*

2   A FAREWELL TO ARMS by Ernest Hemingway
3   POET'S PUB by Eric Linklater
4   MADAME CLAIRE by Susan Ertz
8   WILLIAM by E. H. Young
9   GONE TO EARTH by Mary Webb
12   THE PURPLE LAND by W. H. Hudson
13   PATROL by Philip Macdonald
15   FOUR FRIGHTENED PEOPLE by E. Arnot Robertson
16   THE EDWARDIANS by V. Sackville-West
17   THE INFORMER by Liam O'Flaherty
19   THE STRANGE CASE OF MISS ANNIE SPRAGG by Louis Bromfield
23   ESTHER WATERS by George Moore
24   HANGMAN'S HOUSE by Donn Byrne
27   MY MAN JEEVES by P. G. Wodehouse
28   THE OWLS' HOUSE by Crosbie Garstin
39   THE WALLET OF KAI LUNG by Ernest Bramah
41   CROME YELLOW by Aldous Huxley
42   DEATH OF A HERO by Richard Aldington
43   A SAFETY MATCH by Ian Hay
44   A CUCKOO IN THE NEST by Ben Travers
45   THE GLEN O' WEEPING by Marjorie Bowen
47   THE LONELY PLOUGH by Constance Holme
48   A PASSAGE TO INDIA by E. M. Forster
49   THE JUNGLE by Upton Sinclair
50   THE W PLAN by Graham Seton
52   THE SPANISH FARM by R. H. Mottram
53   DUSTY ANSWER by Rosamond Lehmann
54   I AM JONATHAN SCRIVENER by Claude Houghton
57   THE BLACK DIAMOND by Francis Brett Young
59   THREE WIVES by Beatrice Kean Seymour
72   STILL SHE WISHED FOR COMPANY by Margaret Irwin

FICTION (continued)

73 MR. WESTON'S GOOD WINE by T. F. Powys
75 DECLINE AND FALL by Evelyn Waugh
76 DANGEROUS AGES by Rose Macaulay
80 THE DAWN OF RECKONING by James Hilton
81 TARKA THE OTTER by Henry Williamson
83 THE POACHER by H. E. Bates
84 LOLLY WILLOWES by Sylvia Townsend Warner
85 SIR ISUMBRAS AT THE FORD by D. K. Broster
86 THESE CHARMING PEOPLE by Michael Arlen
87 GREENERY STREET by Denis Mackail
88 THE GREEN LACQUER PAVILION by Helen Beauclerk
91 GHOST STORIES OF AN ANTIQUARY by M. R. James
92 THE HAMPDENSHIRE WONDER by J. D. Beresford
93 WILD STRAWBERRIES by Angela Thirkell
94 SATURDAY NIGHT AT THE GREYHOUND by John Hampson
95 THE MAN WHO WAS THURSDAY by G. K. Chesterton
96 SELECTED MODERN SHORT STORIES selected by Alan Steele
97 SOME EXPERIENCES OF AN IRISH R.M. by Somerville and Ross
102 YOUTH RIDES OUT by Beatrice Kean Seymour
103 A TALL SHIP by "Bartimeus"
104 DEEP WATERS by W. W. Jacobs
105 MANTRAP by Sinclair Lewis
106 NOW EAST, NOW WEST by Susan Ertz
107 PRIVATE WORLDS by Phyllis Bottome
108 KAI LUNG UNROLLS HIS MAT by Ernest Bramah
109 THE FIDDLER by Sarah Gertrude Millin
112 CHILDREN OF THE EARTH by Ethel Mannin
120 PENGUIN PARADE (!)—New Stories
121–2 LEAN MEN by Ralph Bates (in two volumes)
123 SOLDIERS' PAY by William Faulkner
125 AN INDIAN DAY by Edward Thompson
132 MR. PERRIN AND MR. TRAILL by Hugh Walpole

FICTION (continued)

134 CARL AND ANNA and IN THE LAST COACH by Leonhard Frank

135 SEVEN RED SUNDAYS by Ramon J. Sender

136 VILE BODIES by Evelyn Waugh

138 SELF by Beverley Nichols

140 COLD COMFORT FARM by Stella Gibbons

CRIME FICTION *green covers*

5 THE UNPLEASANTNESS AT THE BELLONA CLUB by Dorothy L. Sayers

6 THE MURDER ON THE LINKS by Agatha Christie

34 MR. FORTUNE, PLEASE by H. C. Bailey

58 THE POISONED CHOCOLATES CASE by Anthony Berkeley

61 THE MYSTERIOUS AFFAIR AT STYLES by Agatha Christie

62 THE MISSING MONEYLENDER by W. Stanley Sykes

64 THE FOUR JUST MEN by Edgar Wallace

65 THE MAN IN THE DARK by John Ferguson

78 TRENT'S LAST CASE by E. C. Bentley

79 THE RASP by Philip Macdonald

89 THE DOCUMENTS IN THE CASE by Dorothy L. Sayers (with Robert Eustace)

90 THE SANFIELD SCANDAL by Richard Keverne

98 THE MURDERS IN PRAED STREET by John Rhode

101 MR. JUSTICE RAFFLES by E. W. Hornung

111 THE HOUND OF THE BASKERVILLES by A. Conan Doyle

124 IT WALKS BY NIGHT by John Dickson Carr

127 THE HAVERING PLOT by Richard Keverne

131 TEN MINUTE ALIBI by Anthony Armstrong

137 DEATH AT SWAYTHLING COURT by J. J. Connington

TRAVEL & ADVENTURE *cerise covers*

60 THE DARK INVADER by Captain von Rintelen

66 THE SURGEON'S LOG by J. Johnston Abraham

TRAVEL & ADVENTURE (continued)

67 MY SOUTH SEA ISLAND by Eric Muspratt
68 WITH MYSTICS AND MAGICIANS IN TIBET by Alexandra
      David-Neel
69 ⎫ SOME EXPERIENCES OF A NEW GUINEA RESIDENT
70 ⎭   MAGISTRATE by C. A. W. Monckton (in two volumes)
82 UNDERTONES OF WAR by Edmund Blunden
99 ⎫ THE WORST JOURNEY IN THE WORLD : ANTARCTIC
100 ⎭   1910–1913 by Apsley Cherry-Garrard (in two volumes)
113 THE SECRET OF THE SAHARA by Rosita Forbes
126 TRADER HORN by Alfred Aloysius Horn
133 WATKINS' LAST EXPEDITION by F. Spencer Chapman
139 FLYING DUTCHMAN by Anthony Fokker

BIOGRAPHY & MEMOIRS *dark blue covers*

1 ARIEL by André Maurois
7 TWENTY-FIVE by Beverley Nichols
29–30 AUTOBIOGRAPHY by Margot Asquith
71 CONFESSIONS AND IMPRESSIONS by Ethel Mannin
77 GREY WOLF : MUSTAFA KEMAL by H. C. Armstrong
110 DISRAELI by André Maurois
114–115 FOCH : MAN OF ORLEANS by B. H. Liddell Hart
128 LORD OF ARABIA: IBN SAUD by H. C. Armstrong

MISCELLANEOUS *yellow covers*

116 ON ENGLAND by Stanley Baldwin
118 WHILE ROME BURNS by Alexander Woollcott
119 BILLIARDS AND SNOOKER FOR AMATEUR PLAYERS by
      Horace Lindrum
129–130 THE WEEK-END BOOK (in two volumes)

DRAMA *red covers*

117 SEVEN FAMOUS ONE-ACT PLAYS

PENGUIN SPECIALS

S1 GERMANY PUTS THE CLOCK BACK by Edgar Mowrer
S2 — (to be announced)
S3 — (to be announced)

THE PENGUIN SHAKESPEARE
Specially edited for Penguin Books by Dr. G. B. Harrison.

B 1 TWELFTH NIGHT	B 10 ROMEO AND JULIET
B 2 HAMLET	B 11 JULIUS CAESAR
B 3 HENRY THE FIFTH	B 12 MACBETH
B 4 KING LEAR	B 13 HENRY IV, part i
B 5 AS YOU LIKE IT	B 14 HENRY IV, part ii
B 6 A MIDSUMMER NIGHT'S DREAM	B 15 MUCH ADO ABOUT NOTHING
B 7 THE TEMPEST	B 16 OTHELLO
B 8 THE MERCHANT OF VENICE	B 17 ANTONY AND CLEOPATRA
B 9 RICHARD II	B 18 THE SONNETS

Other volumes to follow shortly.

PELICAN BOOKS *light blue covers*

A series of books on science, economics, history, sociology, archæology, etc. Edited by V. K. Krishna Menon ;—*advisory editors* : H. L. Beales, Reader in Economic History, University of London ; W. E. Williams, Secretary, the British Institute of Adult Education ; Sir Peter Chalmers-Mitchell, Secretary of the Zoological Society, London, 1903–35.

A 1
A 2 } THE INTELLIGENT WOMAN'S GUIDE TO SOCIALISM, CAPITALISM, SOVIETISM AND FASCISM by Bernard Shaw (in two volumes)

A 3 LAST AND FIRST MEN by Olaf Stapledon

A 4 DIGGING UP THE PAST by Sir Leonard Woolley (*with 32 half-tone plates*)

A 5 A SHORT HISTORY OF THE WORLD by H. G. Wells (*with numerous maps*)

A 6 PRACTICAL ECONOMICS by G. D. H. Cole (*first publication*)

A 7 ESSAYS IN POPULAR SCIENCE by Julian Huxley (*illustrated*)

A 8 THE FLOATING REPUBLIC by Dobrée and Manwaring (*The mutinies at the Nore and Spithead in 1797*)

A 9 A HISTORY OF THE ENGLISH PEOPLE (I) by Elie Halévy

PELICAN BOOKS (continued)

A 10 THE MYSTERIOUS UNIVERSE by Sir James Jeans (*with 2 half-tone plates*)

A 11 THE GREAT VICTORIANS (I) edited by H. J. and Hugh Massingham

A 12 THE INEQUALITY OF MAN by J. B. S. Haldane

A 13 LIBERTY IN THE MODERN STATE by Harold J. Laski (*with new introduction*)

A 14 SOCIAL LIFE IN THE INSECT WORLD by J. H. Fabre (*with 15 half-tone plates*)

A 15 THE GROWTH OF CIVILISATION by W. J. Perry (*with several maps*)

A 16 A HISTORY OF THE ENGLISH PEOPLE (II) by Elie Halévy

A 17 A BOOK OF ENGLISH POETRY collected by G. B. Harrison (*a new anthology*)

A 18 AFTER THE DELUGE by Leonard Woolf

A 19 MEDIEVAL PEOPLE by Eileen Power (*with 8 half-tone plates*)

A 20 VISION AND DESIGN by Roger Fry

A 21-2 AN OUTLINE OF THE UNIVERSE by J. G. Crowther (*in two volumes, with numerous illustrations*)

A 23 RELIGION AND THE RISE OF CAPITALISM by R. H. Tawney

A 24 THE PSYCHOPATHOLOGY OF EVERYDAY LIFE by Sigmund Freud

A 25-6 ONLY YESTERDAY by F. L. Allen (2 *volumes, illustrated*)

A 27 UR OF THE CHALDEES by Sir Leonard Woolley (*with 16 half-tone illustrations*)

A 28 CIVILISATION by Clive Bell

A 29 LIMITATIONS OF SCIENCE by J. W. N. Sullivan

A 30 A HISTORY OF THE ENGLISH PEOPLE (III) by Elie Halévy

More volumes to follow.

N.B.

New volumes are continually being added to Penguin and Pelican Books. Please ask your bookseller for the latest list, as further volumes may have been issued since this book was printed. Suggestions of books for inclusion in the series are always welcome.

PELMANISM

PELMANISM is a system of training the mind on scientific lines. It has sometimes been described as "Psychology made popular and practical," but it is something more than that. The system is taught through the medium of fifteen "little grey books" which are accompanied by examination papers. After studying the first of these books, the student answers the accompanying examination paper to the best of his or her ability, and this paper is sent up to an examiner, who marks it and adds appropriate comments. Then the second book is taken, and so the Course continues until the fifteen lessons are completed.

A course of Pelmanism brings out the mind's latent powers and develops them to the highest point of efficiency. It banishes such weaknesses and defects as:

Depression	Mind-Wandering	Weakness of Will
Unnecessary Fears	"Inferiority Complex"	Procrastination
Indefiniteness	Pessimism	Forgetfulness

which interfere with the effective working powers of the mind, and in their place it develops strong, positive, vital qualities such as:

—Optimism	—Will-Power	—Reliability
—Concentration	—Tact	—Decision
—Judgment	—Initiative	—Self-Confidence

By developing these qualities Pelmanism certainly adds to your Efficiency and consequently to your Earning Power.

But what is equally important, Pelmanism increases your happiness and enables you to develop a finer appreciation of the beauties of Nature, the Arts, and Life generally. In a sentence, Pelmanism enables you to live a fuller, richer, happier and more successful existence.

"The Science of Success"—Free

The Pelman System is fully explained in a little book entitled "The Science of Success." The Course is simple and interesting and takes up very little time, and, you can enrol on the most convenient terms. The book will be sent post free on application to-day to—

Pelman Institute

(Established 40 years)

252 Pelman House, Bloomsbury Street, London W.C.1.

PELMAN (OVERSEAS) INSTITUTES : PARIS, 80 Boulevard Haussmann. NEW YORK : 271 North Avenue, New Rochelle. MELBOURNE, 396 Flinders Lane. JOHANNESBURG, P.O. Box 4928. DURBAN, Natal Bank Chambers (P.O. Box 1489). DELHI, 10 Alipore Road. CALCUTTA, 102 Clive Street. AMSTERDAM, Damrak, 68. JAVA, Malabarweg, Malang.